PASTEUR AND MODERN SCIENCE

Books by René Dubos

THE BACTERIAL CELL

BACTERIAL AND MYCOTIC INFECTIONS OF MAN

LOUIS PASTEUR: Free Lance of Science

BIOCHEMICAL DETERMINANTS OF
  MICROBIAL DISEASE

THE MIRAGE OF HEALTH: Utopias, Progress,
  and Biological Change

By René and Jean Dubos

THE WHITE PLAGUE
  Tuberculosis, Man and Society

THE AUTHOR

An eminent microbiologist and experimental pathologist, René Dubos is a member and professor of the Rockefeller Institute in New York City. Born in Saint-Brice, France, in 1901, Dr. Dubos was educated at the Collège Chaptal and Institut National Agronomique in Paris. In 1924, after a few years with the International Institute of Agriculture in Rome, he went to Rutgers University and was awarded his Ph.D. in 1927.

Except for the period 1942–44, when he was George Fabyan Professor of Comparative Pathology and professor of Tropical Medicine at Harvard University Medical School, Dr. Dubos has since 1927 been associated with the Rockefeller Institute, where he did pioneer work in the field of antibiotics. It was Dr. Dubos who first demonstrated the feasibility of obtaining germ-fighting drugs from microbes when, in 1939, he succeeded in isolating from soil a microbe which produced the antibiotics, gramicidin and tyrocidine.

The recipient of many awards for his contributions to science, Dr. Dubos has received honorary degrees from a number of American and European universities. He is a member of the National Acad-

3

emy of Sciences, the Century Association of New York, and the American Philosophical Society. In 1951 he was president of the Harvey Society and the Society of American Bacteriologists.

In addition to his scientific achievements and honors, Dr. Dubos is the author of eight books, the most recent being *The Mirage of Health* (1959), and over 200 articles. Since 1946, he has been editor of the *Journal of Experimental Medicine*.

Dr. Dubos lives with his wife in Garrison, New York.

PASTEUR

AND

MODERN SCIENCE

by RENÉ DUBOS

Published by
Anchor Books
Doubleday & Company, Inc.
Garden City, New York
1960

Available to secondary school
students and teachers through
Wesleyan University Press Incorporated
Columbus 16, Ohio

TYPOGRAPHY BY SUSAN SIEN

THE SCIENCE STUDY SERIES

The Science Study Series offers to students and to the general public the writing of distinguished authors on the most stirring and fundamental topics of physics, from the smallest known particles to the whole universe. Some of the books tell of the role of physics in the world of man, his technology and civilization. Others are biographical in nature, telling the fascinating stories of the great discoverers and their discoveries. All the authors have been selected both for expertness in the fields they discuss and for ability to communicate their special knowledge and their own views in an interesting way. The primary purpose of these books is to provide a survey of physics within the grasp of the young student or the layman. Many of the books, it is hoped, will encourage the reader to make his own investigations of natural phenomena.

These books are published as part of a fresh approach to the teaching and study of physics. At the Massachusetts Institute of Technology during 1956 a group of physicists, high school teachers, journalists, apparatus designers, film producers, and other specialists organized the Physical Sci-

7

ence Study Committee, now operating as a part of Educational Services Incorporated, Watertown, Massachusetts. They pooled their knowledge and experience toward the design and creation of aids to the learning of physics. Initially their effort was supported by the National Science Foundation, which has continued to aid the program. The Ford Foundation, the Fund for the Advancement of Education, and the Alfred P. Sloan Foundation have also given support. The Committee is creating a textbook, an extensive film series, a laboratory guide, especially designed apparatus, and a teacher's source book for a new integrated secondary school physics program which is undergoing continuous evaluation with secondary school teachers.

The Series is guided by a Board of Editors, consisting of Paul F. Brandwein, the Conservation Foundation and Harcourt, Brace and Company; John H. Durston, Educational Services Incorporated; Francis L. Friedman, Massachusetts Institute of Technology; Samuel A. Goudsmit, Brookhaven National Laboratory; Bruce F. Kingsbury, Educational Services Incorporated; Philippe Le-Corbeiller, Harvard University; and Gerard Piel, *Scientific American.*

CONTENTS

The Science Study Series   7

1. FROM SCHOOLBOY TO SCIENTIST   13
   *Birth and Background—A School-
   boy Shows Promise—Pasteur As
   Painter—The Urge for Perfection*

2. A STUDENT OF CRYSTALS   23
   *A Crystallographic Problem — A
   Great Discovery — The Confirma-
   tion: A New Field of Science*

3. SOME ROMANTIC ASPECTS OF PASTEUR'S
   LIFE   31
   *Madame Pasteur: Companion and
   Collaborator — Separating Crystals
   with Molds—The Asymmetry of the
   Universe—Asymmetry and the De-
   velopment of Biochemistry*

4. FROM CRYSTALS TO FERMENTATION   40
   *Living "Ferments"—Sour Milk: The
   Beginning of Scientific Microbiol-
   ogy—One Hundred Years Later*

5. A CROWDED LIFE   50
   *Working Conditions in Paris—A
   Single Gigantic Problem*

6. SPONTANEOUS GENERATION   54
   *Grapes with and without Yeasts—
   The Swan-neck Flask—The Germ
   Theory—The New Science of Bac-
   teriology*

7. PASTEURIZATION   65
   *Wine, Vinegar, and Beer—Partial
   Sterilization or "Pasteurization"—
   New Understanding of Ancient
   Practices*

8. UTILIZING MICROBES   74
   *The Indispensable Links—The Ben-
   efits of Precise Knowledge*

9. BIOCHEMISTRY AND LIFE   81
   *Pasteur Persists—The Discovery of
   "Anaerobic" Life—Point of Synthe-
   sis: The Utilization of Oxygen—A
   Definition of Fermentation—The
   Chemical Mystery of Life*

10. VICTORY OVER DISEASE   94
    *Contagion and the Potato Blight—
    Lister Acknowledges a Debt—Dis-
    eased Silkworms: Another Triumph
    —Personal Tragedy: The Indomita-
    ble Will*

11. THE GERM THEORY IS ESTABLISHED   105
    *Anthrax: A Final Proof—Rabies:
    The Discovery of Filterable Viruses
    —Extension of the Experimental
    Method*

CONTENTS

12. THE BIRTH OF IMMUNOLOGY   113
    *The Origins of Vaccination—From
    Vision to Practice—The Dramatic
    Prophylaxis of Rabies—The Dream
    of "Chemical Vaccines" — From
    Folklore to Knowledge*

13. FURTHER APPLICATIONS OF THE GERM
    THEORY OF DISEASE   128
    *Biological Control and Warfare with
    Microbes—Antibiotics and Aseptic
    Surgery—A Neglected Lesson—The
    Importance of "Terrain"—Physiol-
    ogy and Infection*

14. A DEDICATED LIFE   140
    *Pasteur and Family—Pasteur and
    Country—A Higher Dedication—
    Of His Time and Timeless*

INDEX   153

Chapter 1

From Schoolboy to Scientist

In every country, and in every civilized language, the word *pasteurization* is now part of the vocabulary, just as meaningful to the housewife as it is to the food technologist and to the research bacteriologist. This, of course, represents only one of Louis Pasteur's titles to fame, for his name is associated with some of the largest theoretical concepts and most practical applications of modern science. Thus, biochemists still discuss the metabolic reaction known as the "Pasteur effect," and physicians know that Pasteur's experiments on vaccination constitute one of the landmarks in medical history.

Pasteur's spectacular discoveries are only one of the aspects of his life that have contributed to his immense and universal fame. Equally important is the fact that, in addition to being a great scientist, he was a crusader, concerned as passionately with the welfare of mankind as he was with the search for abstract truth—always ready to engage in public debates and, if need be, in painful struggles, until he had made the world share his convictions, and act upon them. Among his contemporaries there were some who contributed as much as he to scientific progress, but of him it was said, "He was the most perfect man who ever entered the kingdom of Science." To achieve mastery over nature through the use of Science became for him a holy mission—a cause to which he devoted himself with astounding success and with religious fervor. Having become a legendary character even in his own lifetime, he has remained ever since in the public mind the "White Knight of Science."

I have discussed in an earlier book* the development of Pasteur's genius, the philosophical, historical, and social factors that determined the problems on which he worked and his attitude toward them, the intellectual mechanisms of his discoveries, and the emotional atmosphere enveloping them. In the present volume I shall consider some of these problems again, but from a different point of view. I shall emphasize here the relevance of Pasteur's work to certain aspects of modern science and social technology, and try to extrapolate his influence into the future. To do this, however, it will be necessary that we look into the past, for there cannot be any prospect, or even perspective, without retrospect.

* *Louis Pasteur, Free Lance of Science,* Little, Brown and Company, 1950.

14

Birth and Background

Louis Pasteur was born on December 27, 1822, in the small town of Dôle in the eastern part of France. His father had been a sergeant in Napoleon's armies and after returning to civilian life had opened a small tannery in his own house. The elder Pasteur was obviously a man of high ideals, concerned less with earthly riches than with the dignity of human life, and even if he could give his son little in a material way, this much at least he could pass along.

A few historical facts might help to place the year of Pasteur's birth in relation to other events in the world. In 1821, Napoleon I had died in exile on the island rock of St. Helena. Between 1818 and 1823 Brazil, Argentina, and Peru became independent; Mexico, Colombia, Venezuela, and Ecuador were proclaimed republics; the Monroe Doctrine was formulated. The new state of Liberia was founded, and Greece began to struggle for her freedom. Any historical account of the nineteenth century will mention various other political events that occurred in these five years. You will be hard put to find in the standard school histories of the last century more than one reference to science—namely, that in 1819 steam navigation began between Europe and America. Yet the same period had witnessed several extraordinary scientific events which attracted little attention at the time. In Copenhagen, Hans Christian Oersted had found that an electric current tended to twist a magnetic pole around it; and in Paris Ampère had developed further the theory of the interaction between currents and magnets, pointing out the potential use of the phenomenon for telegraphic transmission. In England the great experimenter Michael Faraday had showed that a wire carrying a current could be made to rotate around the pole of a magnet—thus making possible the electric motor.

I have mentioned all these apparently unrelated facts to bring out three points. The first is that Pasteur was born in very exciting times—fully as exciting as our own, both politically and scientifically. The second is that the most important events of the period were not those that attracted public attention. Oersted, Ampère, and Faraday certainly did not make the front page in the newspapers of their day, and few people were aware of their names or even of their existence. Yet, there is no doubt that their achievements did more to revolutionize the ways of life all over the world than did the contemporary political revolutions. Third, it is not without interest to reflect on the fact that Michael Faraday, who occupies in the physico-chemical sciences much the same place that Pasteur occupies in biochemistry, biology, and medicine, also was born in very humble circumstances. Both Pasteur and Faraday had many occasions to capitalize on their fame and to acquire wealth from the practical applications of their discoveries. Yet both resisted the temptation for the sake of higher values. It is worth noting that both of them received official recognition fairly early in life, a fact which shows that thoughtful men of the nineteenth century were already conscious of the social importance of science.

A Schoolboy Shows Promise

The young Louis Pasteur lived the typical life of a French boy in humble small-town surroundings. He seems to have been a serious, well-behaved child, devoted to his family, perhaps a little pompous if we can judge from the sermonizing letters that he wrote to his sisters. There is no indication that he was an especially brilliant student in school, but certainly he was diligent, thorough in his studies, and determined to fulfill his father's ambition—or dream—that he should become some sort of a scholar. What kind of a scholar? No one around him knew exactly. It was enough for his family to imagine that Louis would be a professor of some sort, because there was great social distinction in those days in being a professor. In fact, Louis eventually reached the famous Ecole Normale Supérieure in Paris, a school devoted to the training of college professors in literature, arts, and sciences. Although he displayed great promise as an artist, he elected to work in science.

The school records show that he did very well at the Ecole Normale Supérieure. Let me here take a malicious pleasure in quoting what his professors had to say when he was graduated from the school. "Will make a good professor," was their official comment in the school records. Their judgment was right in the sense that Pasteur became an excellent teacher, thorough in preparation and effective in delivery. Yet it was not as a professor that he would be remembered, but as a man whose discoveries would contribute immensely to human welfare. At this point, let me quote another opinion expressed by teachers concerning a young man who also was to achieve immense fame. When Napoleon Bonaparte was graduated at the age of eighteen from the Brienne Military Academy, his teachers sent him off with the statement, "Will go far, if circumstances favor him"—a truly prophetic judgment!

Pasteur, however, would not need to be favored by circumstances. At every step in his life Pasteur chose to take his stand against the odds, often at the cost of immense struggles and sacrifices. Whatever the circumstances in which he had to work, he never submitted to them, but instead molded them to the demands of his imagination and his will.

Pasteur As Painter

Of Pasteur's school years I shall confine myself to a few aspects, selected because they reveal traits of character that contributed later to his effectiveness as a scientist. Very early in life Pasteur displayed great skill at drawing and painting. Portraits of his father and mother that he painted at the age of thirteen reveal forcefulness and mastery of style. No sign here of the freewheeling art of modern children, but clearly a disciplined and successful effort to represent what his parents looked like physically, and what they stood for in the eyes of their fellow citizens. Until he was nineteen, he continued to draw portraits of the townspeople and of his school friends, and professional artists have testified to the technical excellence of these works. The Finnish artist Albert Edelfeldt, who painted a famous portrait of Pasteur in his laboratory in 1887, expressed in a letter the following judgment on Pasteur as a painter: "Outside of science, painting is one of the few things that interest him. At the age of sixteen, he had intended to become a painter and amused himself making pastel drawings of his parents and of other citizens of Arbois; I have looked at these pastels very often. They are extremely good and drawn with energy, full of character, a little dry in color, but far superior to the usual work of young people who destine themselves to an artistic career. There is something of the great analyst in these portraits: they express absolute truth and uncommon will power. I am certain that had M. Pasteur selected art instead of science, France would count today one more able painter. . . ."

Looking at Pasteur's painting, one perceives the power of observation and concentration which was such an important part of his scientific endowment, but one cannot help noticing also another fact which certainly tells something of his character and of the environment in which he lived—the dignity of the sitters, and the seriousness of their expression. Clearly the acquaintances of the Pasteur family were solid citizens and clearly also the young Pasteur regarded life as a very serious matter. There is not a single smile in the twenty-odd portraits by him that I have seen. Interestingly enough, only one of his own photographs shows a smiling face. It shows Pasteur in the company of a colleague who tried to convince him that beer should not be regarded as a problem in fermentation alone, but also as a source of good cheer.

There is still another point of interest about Pasteur as a portrait painter. He intended at one time to become a professional artist, but at the age of nineteen he stopped painting abruptly and forever, obviously having decided that nothing should compete with his scientific work. And, in fact, nothing ever did. Except for summer vacations that he always spent at his family home in the country, he never took time off from work, cultivating no hobby and having no known vice or even a weakness. He was probably the most dedicated servant that science ever had.

The Urge for Perfection

Admission to the Ecole Normale Supérieure was by competitive examination, and in 1842, Pasteur was declared admissible, sixteenth in rank.

For anyone else this would have been a very satisfactory result, but not for him. In a gesture which is probably unique, or in any case extremely rare, he refused admission to the school and took up his studies again to prepare himself better. He competed again in 1843, was fifth in rank, and this time entered the school. The urge for perfection revealed by this detail was to remain one of the dominant traits of his scientific career.

At the Ecole Normale, Pasteur specialized in the section of physics and chemistry, and it is in this field that he won his first laurels. This fact is worth noting because his early specialization did not deter him from moving shortly after into purely biological fields. What Pasteur gained in school was a strong theoretical background and, more importantly, an exacting intellectual discipline. On this broad and solid basis he built the structure that led him step by step from theoretic studies on the physico-chemical properties of crystals, through prophetic discoveries on respiration and fermentation, to the most practical problems of vaccination and public health. In the course of the following pages, I shall attempt to show how this theoretical knowledge and intellectual discipline were illustrated in Pasteur's scientific life. As you will see, he never shied away from the problems that chance, and the times, placed across his way—however remote they were from his past experience. Although trained as a chemist, he was willing to venture into purely biological fields because of his profound confidence that the experimental method, of which he was a master, was applicable to all types of inquiry, and that the specialized knowledge required for each particular question could be acquired by diligent effort.

As an introduction to the review of Pasteur's scientific achievements, let me quote from a famous speech that he delivered late in life—in 1882—on the occasion of his being received as a member of the august French Academy of Letters. Appearing before literary men, philosophers, and historians, he expressed with his usual forcefulness the reasons that made him a devotee of science. He pointed out that while the experimental method may never be able to solve completely the riddle of the universe, it can always answer an unambiguous yes or no to well-defined questions asked in unambiguous terms. Facing the skeptical philosopher Ernest Renan, who was receiving him at the Académie Française, he spoke of "this marvelous experimental method, of which one can say, in truth, not that it is sufficient for every purpose, but that it rarely leads astray, and then only those who do not use it well. It eliminates certain facts, brings forth others, interrogates nature, compels it to reply and stops only when the mind is fully satisfied. The charm of our studies, the enchantment of science, is that, everywhere and always, we can give the justification of our principles and the proof of our discoveries."

Chapter 2

A Student of Crystals

In 1847 Pasteur buckled down to research work for his doctor's degree at the Ecole Normale Supérieure. He was then twenty-four and letters of the time to his boyhood friend Chappuis leave no doubt that, even so early in his career, there was deep in his heart the secret desire to accomplish some great feat. The problem that was then in his mind, as we shall see later, was the very origin of life on earth. In point of fact, however, the selection of his research project was not determined by some genial inspiration, or even by a philosophical preoccupation with some deep problem. As is the case with most graduate students, his project certainly arose from discussions that went on at the Ecole Normale among his schoolmates under the influence of teachers whom they respected. Problems of crystallography were then scientifically fashionable, and Pasteur showed no originality in electing to work on them for his doctor's thesis. But his originality began to become manifest as he went deeper into this field. His career illustrates well that what an individual achieves in life depends less upon the circumstances in which he has to function than upon what he brings to bear upon them. Napoleon meant something of this sort when he wrote in his diary, "No situation is good or bad in itself, everything depends upon what one makes out of it."

A Crystallographic Problem

In the science department at the Ecole Normale, there was much interest in the problems of crystallography, and Delafosse, one of the most respected teachers, had made significant observations revealing the existence in quartz crystals of right- and left-handed* facets. It was also known at the time that quartz in the crystalline state can rotate the plane of polarized light.* Jean Baptiste Biot, a celebrated French chemist who was to become one of Pasteur's scientific protectors, had shown furthermore that certain organic substances like sugar or tartaric acid can also rotate the plane of light but, in contrast to quartz, exhibit optical activity even in solution. All these facts were much discussed at the Ecole Normale and it was under this influence that Pasteur began to work on the optical activity of crystals. He selected tartaric acid and

* For a discussion of these crystal properties see *Crystals and Crystal Growing*, by Alan Holden and Phylis Singer (Science Study Series).

tartrates as the object of his studies because a great deal was known about these substances, and also because they readily gave beautiful crystalline forms.

At precisely that time Jean Baptiste Biot presented before the Academy of Sciences in Paris a note in which the German chemist Mitscherlich described a very odd fact concerning the optical activity of tartrates. Mitscherlich pointed out that among the usual large crystals of tartaric acid always present in the "tartar" formed during the fermentation of wine, there were found occasionally smaller crystals, needlelike tufts, which proved to be another form of tartaric acid. The latter form was called "paratartaric acid" or also "racemic" acid to recall its origin from the grape (*racemus*). According to Mitscherlich, these two forms of tartaric acids and their respective salts, the tartrates and paratartrates, had "the same chemical composition, the same crystal shape with the same angles, the same specific gravity, the same double refraction, and therefore the same angles between their optical axes. Their aqueous solutions have the same refraction. But the solution of the tartrate rotates the plane of polarization, while the paratartrate is inactive."

Pasteur immediately saw an incompatibility here. Could the two forms of tartaric acid behave differently toward polarized light and still, according to Mitscherlich's claim, be identical in every other particular? He was convinced that there *had* to be some chemical difference between the two substances, and he hoped that this difference would express itself in the shape of the crystals. It was the recognition of this incompatibility that provided him with the first well-defined problem on which to test his skill as an experimenter. By seizing on the occasion, he demonstrated one of the most fundamental characteristics of the gifted experimenter: the ability to recognize an important problem, and to formulate it in terms amenable to experimentation.

A Great Discovery

Immediately and without help, Pasteur prepared and crystallized nineteen different salts of tartrates and paratartrates, and examined the crystals with great care under the microscope. With much satisfaction he found that they all exhibited small facets similar to those seen in quartz crystals —a fact which had escaped the attention of other observers. Then he detected that these facets did not all have the same orientation in the different crystals. More precisely, the facets in each of the tartrate salts exhibited the same orientation, whereas in each of the paratartrates, some were oriented in one direction, and some in the opposite direction. But at this point it seems best to let Pasteur describe in his own words how he made the discovery that launched him on a scientific career.

"The fortunate idea came to me to orient my crystals with reference to a plane perpendicular to the observer, and then I noticed that the confused mass of crystals of paratartrate could be divided into two groups according to the orientation of their facets of asymmetry. In one group, the facet of asymmetry nearer my body was inclined to my right with reference to the plane of orientation which I just mentioned, whereas the facet of asymmetry was inclined to my left in the other. The paratartrate appeared as a mixture of two kinds of crystals, some asymmetric to the right, some asymmetric to the left.

"A new and obvious idea soon occurred to me. These crystals asymmetric to the right, which I could separate manually from the others, exhibited an absolute identity of shape with those of the classical right tartrate. Pursuing my preconceived idea, in the logic of its deductions, I separated these right crystals from the crystallized paratartrate; I made the lead salt and isolated the acid; this acid appeared absolutely identical with the tartaric acid of grape, identical also in its action on polarized light. My happiness was even greater the day when, separating now from the paratartrate the crystals with asymmetry at their left, and making their acid, I obtained a tartaric absolutely similar to the tartaric acid of grape, but with an opposite asymmetry, and also with an opposite action on light. Its shape was identical to that of the mirror image of the right tartaric acid and, other things being equal, it rotated light to the left as much in absolute amount as the other acid did it to the right.

"Finally, when I mixed solutions containing equal weights of these two acids, the mixture gave rise to a crystalline mass of paratartaric acid identical with the known paratartaric acid."

It is easy to recapture the dramatic quality of the situation and the intense excitement it must have caused in the young investigator. Pasteur was so overcome with emotion that he rushed from the laboratory, and, meeting one of the chemistry assistants in the hall, embraced him, exclaiming, "I have just made a great discovery. . . . I am so happy that I am shaking all over and am unable to set my eyes again to the polarimeter!" To appreciate the magnitude of the achievement, it must be remembered that Pasteur was then barely twenty-five years old and had been working in a laboratory for only two years. Let us keep in mind also that this laboratory was very small and very primitive according to modern standards. Not only did Pasteur have to prepare all the chemicals that he used, he even had to build with his own hands the polarimeter and the goniometer with which he made his measurements. He had no assistance, only the encouragement of his teachers and school friends, and faith in his destiny.

The Confirmation: A New Field of Science

The news of Pasteur's discovery soon spread through the Paris scientific circles and eventually reached Jean Baptiste Biot—the very man who three years before had presented to the Academy of Sciences the Mitscherlich paper which had perplexed Pasteur and had served him as a springboard for his studies. Biot was so much interested in the new discovery that he was willing to present it to the scientific public, but before he did, he wanted to subject the findings to a stringent verification. Here again, let us read Pasteur's own account of his dealings with Biot.

"He [M. Biot] sent for me to repeat before his eyes the several experiments and gave me a sample of racemic acid which he had himself previously examined and found to be quite inactive toward polarized light. I prepared from it, in his presence, the sodium ammonium double salt, for which he also desired himself to provide the soda and ammonia. The solution was set aside for slow evaporation in one of the rooms of his own laboratory, and when thirty to forty grams of crystals had separated, he again summoned me to the College de France [where Biot had his office] so that I might collect the dextro and levorotatory crystals [i.e., the crystals deviating the plane of polarized light to the right or to the left] before his eyes, and separate them according to their crystallographic character—asking me to repeat the statement that the crystals which I should place on his right hand would cause deviation to the right, and the others to the left. This done, he said that he himself would do the rest. He prepared the carefully weighed solutions, and at the moment when he was about to examine them in the polarimeter, he again called me into his laboratory. He first put into the apparatus the more interesting solution, the one which was to cause rotation to the left. At the first sight of the color tints presented by the two halves of the field in the "Soleil" polarimeter, and without having to make a reading, Biot recognized that there was a strong levorotation. Then the illustrious old man, who was visibly moved, seized me by the hand, and said, 'My dear son, I have loved science so deeply that this stirs my heart.'"

Thus, at one stroke Pasteur had established himself as a masterful experimenter and created a new field of science—namely the relation of optical activity to molecular and crystalline structure. For three years he continued in this field and made concrete and lasting contributions to the chemical aspects of crystallography. But instead of following his work in detail, let us now turn to some more romantic aspects of his life.

Chapter 3

Some Romantic Aspects of Pasteur's Life

On the completion of his postgraduate work Pasteur left the Ecole Normale, and in 1848 he was appointed professor of chemistry at the University of Strassburg. There he was introduced into the family of one of the university officials, and within a few weeks after having met the young daughter of the family, Marie Laurent, he asked her hand in marriage. Thus, he took this most important step of his personal life with the same impetuosity that he was to manifest so often in his scientific career. His work was apparently somewhat disturbed during the few months of his courtship, at least if we believe the letters that he wrote to his fiancée.

"I have not cried so much since the death of my dear mother. I woke up suddenly with the thought that you did not love me and immediately started to cry. . . . My work no longer means anything to me. I, who so much loved my crystals, I who always used to wish in the evening that the night be shorter to come back the sooner to my studies."

Madame Pasteur: Companion and Collaborator

But the disturbance was only of short duration, and it is not apparent that it ever interfered seriously with Pasteur's scientific work. Soon after his marriage, in May 1849, the stream of discoveries began to flow again, as swiftly as before. I shall not speak again of Madame Pasteur, and yet her participation in Pasteur's achievements was much greater than these few lines would suggest. It is the unanimous opinion of all who knew her that she was not only a devoted wife, but also provided an ideal atmosphere for Pasteur's studious life. Gay and modest, she helped him through the many tragedies and struggles of his life, especially after the paralysis which struck him in 1868. She accepted in good spirit his odd mannerisms and the material limitations of their existence. She consecrated herself to his dreams, molding her behavior to fit the goal that he formulated. In other words, she identified her life completely with his work. She could write to her children in 1884: "Your father is absorbed in his thoughts, talks little, sleeps little, rises at dawn, and in one word continues the life I began with him this day thirty-five years ago."

Her intelligent devotion is perhaps best evoked by the words pronounced at the time of her death by Emile Roux, who had been Pasteur's associate for twenty years and had known the couple intimately:

"From the first days of their common life, Madame Pasteur understood what kind of man she had married; she did everything to protect him from the difficulties of life, taking onto herself the worries of the home, that he might retain the full freedom of his mind for his investigations. Madame Pasteur loved her husband to the extent of understanding his studies. During the evenings, she wrote under his dictation, calling for explanations, for she took a genuine interest in crystalline structure or in attenuated viruses. She had become aware that ideas become the clearer for being explained to others, and that nothing is more conducive to devising new experiments than describing the ones which have just been completed. Madame Pasteur was more than an incomparable companion for her husband, she was his best collaborator."

Separating Crystals with Molds

Pasteur's marriage was not the only romantic aspect of his life in Strassburg. Another very different one reveals the complexity of his scientific personality—the constant interplay in his mind between rigorous, logical thinking and highly imaginative dreams about the mysteries of life. Throughout his scientific career, he engaged in thoughts of cosmic grandeur that went far beyond practical realities. But these romantic imaginings were always derived from factual observations, and often they led him to entirely new lines of investigation. It is to this aspect of his genius that we shall now turn.

As will be recalled, Pasteur's first fractionation of racemic acid into its two isomeric components was the painstaking process of separating the crystals under the microscope according to the orientation of their facets. In subsequent years much less laborious methods of separation were worked out in his laboratory, but only one will be mentioned here, a very original method of chemical fractionation based on a biological phenomenon. This method was discovered in 1857, the result of one of those accidents or "chance" occurrences that are meaningless to ordinary persons and are seized upon only by trained observers whose minds are receptive to the clues offered by nature. "In experimental science," Pasteur was wont to say, "chance favors only the prepared mind."

The fact that certain molds grow readily in solutions of calcium paratartrate during warm weather had been frequently observed, and it occurred in Pasteur's laboratory as it did in other places. The common reaction was, of course, to throw the solution down the sink because it was moldy. In contrast, Pasteur asked himself whether the two isomeric components of the solution, the half which rotated light to the left and the half which rotated it to the right, would be differently affected by the mold. To answer this question, he investigated the optical activity of a solution of paratartrate infected with a mold, and found, to his great excitement, that the solution became more active optically with time. He proved that only one of the components (the right rotating) was destroyed, whereas the other component was spared. As a result, the latter component persisted alone in the solution and thus caused it to become optically active. This observation led to an entirely novel and convenient method for the separation of the two isomeric forms by means of the mold, but more importantly it led Pasteur's mind into new channels that were to take him, and science, into completely uncharted territory.

The Asymmetry of the Universe

It was already known that many organic substances, that is, substances produced by living things, have the ability to rotate the plane of polarized light in one direction or the other. In contrast, Pasteur was aware of the fact that if the same substances were synthesized in the laboratory, they were optically inactive. Now it appeared from the experience with paratartaric acid that at least one living thing, a mold, exhibited a striking selectivity with regard to its action on one of the two isomeric components. Putting all these facts together and extrapolating from them, Pasteur soon formed the view that only living agents could produce optically active asymmetric compounds and that an intensive study of molecular asymmetry would eventually throw light on the genesis of life. In his words, "This important criterion [molecular asymmetry] constitutes perhaps the only sharply defined difference which can be drawn at the present time between the chemistry of dead and of living matter." And to his friend Chappuis he confided in 1851, "I am on the verge of mysteries, and the veil which covers them is getting thinner and thinner. The night seems to me too long." These "mysteries" had to do with nothing less than the creation of life! He postulated that the peculiar selectivity of living processes for one or the other of isomeric forms of the same molecule might be the manifestation of asymmetric forces of the environment acting upon the living organism during the synthesis of protoplasmic constituents.

In his words, "Life, as manifested to us, is a function of the asymmetry of the universe and of the consequences of this fact. The universe is asymmetrical; for, if the whole of the bodies which compose the solar system moving with their individual movements were placed before a glass, the image in the glass could not be superposed upon the reality. Even the movement of solar light is asymmetrical. . . . Terrestrial magnetism, the opposition which exists between the north and south poles in a magnet and between positive and negative electricity, are but resultants of asymmetrical actions and movements. . . .

"Life is dominated by asymmetrical actions. I can even imagine that all living species are primordially, in their structure, in their external forms, functions of cosmic asymmetry."

Pasteur was bold enough to attempt some experimentation in this highly speculative domain, hoping to duplicate in the laboratory the asymmetrical effects which he assumed to preside over the synthesis of organic materials in nature. He used powerful magnets in order to introduce asymmetrical influences during the formation of crystals. He also devised a clockwork arrangement with which he intended to reverse the natural movement of the solar rays striking a plant, from its birth to its death. He was thus trying to find out whether in such an artificial world—where the sun rose, so to speak, in the west and set in the east—the optically active substances would not appear in forms opposite to those occurring in the normal order of nature! He eventually abandoned these fantastic experiments without having obtained any results, but never gave up completely his alchemist's dream of unraveling the chemical riddle of life.

Asymmetry and the Development of Biochemistry

I shall not deal further with these experiments, but I cannot refrain from mentioning that even today the fact that asymmetric molecules are always the products of living processes remains as much of a mystery as ever. Ever since Pasteur, it has been universally accepted that molecules with a certain degree of complexity exist in two forms, the structure of one being related to that of the other as

37

the right hand is related to the left so that each is identical with the mirror image of the other. Both forms may occur in living organisms, but as a rule each species uses or synthesizes only one. Such asymmetric syntheses are hard to manage in the laboratory. Pasteur's romantic preoccupation with this problem might acquire some new significance in the near future, since the chemical reactions involved in the origin of life are once more coming to the forefront of scientific preoccupation. One of the contributors to a recent symposium on this subject opened his paper on "The Origin of Optical Activity" with the remark that "no other chemical characteristic is as distinctive of living organisms as is optical activity." It might be mentioned also that the recent discovery of the non-conservation of parity in certain interactions of "fundamental particles" has led to a general acceptance of the notion that the structure of the universe is asymmetrical. This is what Pasteur had prophesied in 1874 before the French Academy of Sciences: "L'univers est un ensemble dissymétrique et je suis persuadé que la vie, telle qu'elle se manifeste à nous, est fonction de la dissymétrie de l'univers ou des consequences qu'elle entraine. *L'univers est dissymétrique.*"

While Pasteur's studies on the biological significance of stereoisomerism (from the Greek: *stereos,* solid; *isos,* equal; and *meros,* part) did not explain the genesis of life, they have yielded a number of facts which have had far-reaching influence on the development of biochemistry. Pasteur himself recognized that the differences in structural configuration between the isomeric forms of tartaric acids, as well as of other organic compounds, are reflected in the differential behavior of these isomeric substances toward living agents, for example, in their effect on taste buds and in their susceptibility to attack by microorganisms. These observations have served as a springboard for a whole range of investigations on the chemical basis of biological specificity, a problem which is such a characteristic feature of modern biochemistry.

Although we cannot develop here the implications of the fact that biological activity is dependent on molecular structure, we must deal further with the very direct and profound influence that this phenomenon had on Pasteur's scientific life. It can truly be said, as we shall now see, that it was from his conviction that asymmetric molecules are always the product of life that he was led to the study of fermentation, to the recognition that microorganisms play an essential role in the economy of nature, and eventually to his epoch-making discoveries in the field of infectious diseases.

Chapter 4

From Crystals to Fermentation

In Strassburg recognition had come to Pasteur in the form of honors and prizes. Although he used the money thus earned to buy laboratory equipment—at the sacrifice of many urgent needs at home—his working facilities were still extremely limited. For this reason, he accepted the offer that was made to him in 1854 to take the chair of chemistry and to become dean of sciences in the newly organized University of Lille, in the north of France. It was understood that he should focus his teaching and other activities on the industrial interests of the Lille region. The surviving notes for his lectures in chemistry show that he took this recommendation to heart. It may be instructive that the requirement to teach the industrial applications of chemistry led him to develop a philosophy of science that guided him for the rest of his life.

Heretofore Pasteur had been a purely theoretical scientist, unconcerned with practical matters, and now he had to take an active interest in local industries. This appeared to create a conflict of interest between his former life and his new position, for then, as now, there were many who believed that the state of mind required for the successful prosecution of pure science was almost incompatible with the attitude imposed by applied science. But this was not Pasteur's opinion. Immediately he formulated the view, and taught it with passion to his students, that in fact there was no incompatibility. In his words, "There are not two different kinds of science; there is science and there are the applications of science." The two types constantly interplay, and one type cannot progress far without contact with the other. Nor were these idle words, for within one year after his arrival in Lille he had begun to concern himself with the practical problems of alcoholic fermentation, which was one of the chief industries of the region. From his investigations he derived clues for his theoretical problems, and soon was able to apply his new knowledge to the improvement of factory practices. As we shall see later, he retained the same philosophy throughout his life, whether he dealt with the manufacture of beer, the preservation of wine, the diseases of silkworms, or the problems of vaccination.

Living "Ferments"

Shortly after his arrival in Lille, Pasteur was approached by an industrialist named Bigo, who was engaged in the production of alcohol by the fermentation of beet juice. Monsieur Bigo complained that in many cases, and for unknown reasons, the alcohol became contaminated with undesirable substances in the course of fermentation. Pasteur was totally unfamiliar with the problem of alcoholic fermentation, but nevertheless agreed to look into it. He visited the factory at frequent intervals, observed everything he could, and took samples of the fermenting juice back to his laboratory. Among other tests he put the fermenting juice under the microscope and made careful descriptions and drawings of all that he could see. He noticed in particular, as others had before him, the presence of small globules of yeast in the fermenting juice, but he saw in addition other smaller structures that did not look like yeast. He also examined the juice in his polarimeter and found that it was optically active, capable of rotating the plane of polarized light. One of the optically active components that he could isolate from the fermented beet juice was amyl alcohol. This immediately brought back to his mind one of his earlier interests, his belief that only living things could produce optically active organic compounds. And it was this thought that became the link between his past scientific life in chemistry and his subsequent work in biology. Shortly after finding optically active amyl alcohol in the fermenting juice, he became convinced that, contrary to general belief, the processes involved in fermentation were not merely chemical in character, but came from the activity of living things: of living "ferments" as he used to call them, of microbes or microorganisms as we now say.

At this point, we must stop for a moment to consider what was then regarded as the scientific theory of fermentation, the point of view taught in all standard textbooks. It was known that yeast always accompanied alcoholic fermentation, and several naturalists had recognized under the microscope that yeast had a definite globular shape. But according to the accepted view, yeast was nothing but a complex chemical substance, acting as catalyst in the conversion of sugar into alcohol. With less precision, but much in the same spirit, it was also known that other chemical changes in organic matter—for example, the conversion of sugar into lactic acid, or of alcohol into vinegar—were likewise accompanied by the presence of complex materials, which also were assumed to act as catalysts, purely by chemical contact. This point of view was taught in all textbooks, under the sanction of the most eminent chemists of the day, particularly of Berzelius and Liebig.

The new and very revolutionary suggestion that Pasteur made was that the yeast found during alcoholic fermentation, and the organic material associated with the production of lactic acid and acetic acid, were not lifeless catalysts but in reality were living things. He contended that the organic materials served as food for these living things and that the products accumulating in their presence were the results of their metabolic processes. Thus,

43

many phenomena that theretofore had been considered purely chemical were in his view biological in origin. Let me emphasize that Pasteur's views were at first little more than hunches of the kind that are formulated with much emphasis in heated discussions, and most commonly late in the evening over a glass of beer, but which usually fade in the harsh light of day. If Pasteur had done nothing more than formulate ideas, suggested to him by the fact that optically active substances denote the presence of a living agent, his name would now be forgotten as are the names of so many other young men who have had bright ideas but have done nothing to convert them into realities. Fortunately, Pasteur was disciplined enough to use his hunch as a working hypothesis, as a basis on which to build a solidly documented experimental structure.

Sour Milk: The Beginning of Scientific Microbiology

Here I shall not try to describe or even list the large numbers of experiments that Pasteur devised and carried out, to prove that in his words "fermentation is a phenomenon correlative of life." Rather I shall select one instance because in his view—and rightfully, I believe—it dealt with a situation crucial to the whole argument. This particular case is that of the conversion of sugar into lactic acid. This conversion occurs frequently in nature, for example, in the souring of milk, which most commonly results from the transformation of milk sugar into lactic acid. From the biochemical point of view, nothing could be simpler than this change, since it corresponds to the breakdown of one molecule of glucose into two molecules of lactic acid.

In my opinion (and here I engage in historical mind reading), it was because of its apparently simple chemical character that Pasteur selected this reaction as a test to demonstrate the role of living things in chemical changes. This move illustrates, I believe, the extraordinary sense of scientific showmanship that he displayed so often in life. What Pasteur showed in this first study—as he did even more convincingly with other more complex fermentations—was that the lactic-acid ferment consists of an immense number of microscopic organized bodies, which all resemble one another. Moreover, he demonstrated that these formed bodies could be made to increase in number if he supplied them with the proper kind of food. Once grown in the pure state and in sufficient amount, the lactic ferment could be transferred to a new sugar solution, and then it accomplished with extraordinary speed the transformation of the sugar into lactic acid.

By applying the same experimental approach to other types of fermentation, Pasteur showed furthermore that the acidity, neutrality, or alkalinity of the fermenting solutions had very profound effects on the activity of the various kinds of ferments. Thus, yeast produces alcohol most rapidly in an acid solution, whereas the lactic-acid ferment is most active at neutrality. He even recognized—for the first time—the activity of certain antiseptics. Onion juice, he found, inhibited the action of yeast, but not of the lactic-acid ferment. The ideas of a specific ferment associated with each fermentation, of disproportion between the weight of the ferment produced and the weight of matter transformed, of vital competition between two organisms simultaneously invading the same medium, resulting in the dominance of the one better adapted to the culture conditions—all these ideas, which the future was to prove valid and develop into a body of science and technology, are forcefully set forth in a short paper that he published in 1857 under the title, *Mémoire sur la fermentation appelée lactique*. This paper can truly be regarded as the beginning of scientific microbiology, indeed as one of the most important landmarks of biochemical and biological sciences. Its fundamental spirit can be summarized in Pasteur's own words: "The purity of a ferment, its homogeneity, its free unrestrained development from foodstuffs well adapted to its individual nature, these are some of the conditions which are essential for good fermentation."

One Hundred Years Later

In the light of these concepts, which appear so obvious now, but were so revolutionary 100 years ago, it became possible to explain the defects in the industrial production of alcohol which had first brought Pasteur in direct contact with the problems of fermentation. The small globules of yeast, always associated with alcoholic fermentation, were not just bits of inanimate material catalyzing the conversion of sugar into alcohol. Yeast was a microscopic plant, with a life of its own, and alcohol was the product of its living processes. The other smaller bodies that Pasteur had detected in the defective fermentations were also living organisms. They differed from yeast not only in size and shape, but also in chemical activity, and therefore in the nature of their products. They were the cause of the defects in alcoholic fermentation, and the solution to Monsieur Bigo's difficulties was therefore to eliminate these other microscopic living agents, or to prevent them from gaining a foothold in the fermenting fluid. There were many practical details to be solved before these theoretical considerations could be made the basis of industrial processes. But at least the problem had been clearly stated, and we shall see in the following chapter how practical applications rapidly followed from these beautifully simple concepts.

As already mentioned, the ideas that Pasteur derived from the study of lactic and alcoholic fermentation constitute the fundamental basis of microbiological sciences, and it is truly remarkable that the *Mémoire sur la fermentation appelée lactique,* in which they first appeared, was published hardly more than two years after he had begun to work on the problems of fermentation! In this preliminary paper he even suggested, though without evidence, that the same principles might contribute to the understanding of infectious diseases! In view of the historical importance of this short paper, it is not unusual that the hundredth anniversary of its publication should have been celebrated, in 1957, as marking the beginning of a new era for science and technology. During the celebration many speakers from all over the world emphasized that much of our present knowledge of biochemistry has evolved from the point of view first enunciated by Pasteur with regard to lactic acid and alcoholic fermentation; others showed how this knowledge constitutes the basis of many important biological industries—in particular those concerned with the production of organic substances by microorganisms; still others focused attention upon the medical consequences of the event, the germ theory of disease, and the production of drugs (antibiotics) to combat infection. We shall have occasion to come back to these modern developments, but before proceeding with our story, it may be helpful to place Pasteur's early studies in their historical context.

Let us look at the account of the nineteenth century in the Encyclopedia Americana. For the year 1857 the Encyclopedia mentions three events of particular importance: "The Indian Mutiny—France and England Invade China—Business Panic in the United States." The Encyclopedia makes no reference to Pasteur's *Mémoire sur la fermentation appelée lactique*, nor does it mention other scientific events which also occurred in

1857. In Germany, for example, Rudolf Virchow submitted for publication his epoch-making book *Cellular Pathology*, which revolutionized scientific medical thinking. And in England Charles Darwin wrote a letter to the American botanist Asa Gray, stating in very precise form the ideas that we now call the theory of evolution. For those of us whose lives are devoted to scientific pursuits, it is rather pleasing to note that the Indian mutiny, the invasion of China, and the business panic were even then and have remained ever since identified with unpleasant aspects of human life, whereas the works of Pasteur, Darwin, and Virchow—unnoticed in the account of the nineteenth century in the Encyclopedia—are still today creative forces toward a more enlightened and better world.

Chapter 5

A Crowded Life

In 1857 Pasteur was appointed assistant director in charge of scientific studies and of general administration at his alma mater, the Ecole Normale Supérieure in Paris. In addition to organization of the curriculum, his administrative duties included the supervision of housing, board, medical care, and general discipline of the students, as well as the relations between the school and parents and other educational establishments. As shown by his reports, he did not take these new responsibilities lightly. He administered the problems of household management with as much thoroughness and vigor as he devoted to the reorganization of advanced studies. Moreover, Pasteur, who was now widely known in academic circles, soon became involved in larger problems of national interest. His prestige, and his combative nature, progressively led him into controversies which often went beyond scientific subjects. Yet despite all these interferences, his laboratory work in Paris became even more intense and more productive than it had been in Strassburg and in Lille.

Working Conditions in Paris

Before proceeding to a description of his discoveries during that period, a few words must be said concerning the conditions under which he worked in Paris. His title of director of scientific studies at the Ecole Normale might give the impression that he had at his disposal large and well-equipped laboratories, with many assistants and generous budgets, but in fact he had limited facilities. During the early years after his return to Paris he worked alone and had to make many of his instruments.

He found in the attic of the school two very small unused rooms, and he converted them into a laboratory which he equipped with funds from the family budget. The studies on alcoholic fermentation begun in Lille were completed in these miserable quarters. Eventually he obtained from the authorities an assistant whose time was to be given entirely to investigative work—an arrangement hitherto unheard of in France. He was, furthermore, allowed to move his laboratory into a primitive "pavilion," consisting of five small rooms on two floors, which had been built for the school architect and his clerks. Crowded for space, and pinched for funds, he improvised an incubator under the stairway. The only way he could enter it was by crawling on hands and knees, yet it was in this cramped room that Pasteur spent long hours daily observing the countless flasks with which he convinced the world that "spontaneous generation" was a chimera. After a few years, the small laboratory was enlarged by additional construction, and from these few rooms—so modest by modern standards—came the studies which made Pasteur's name famous in many fields of learning. He could carry out his research work only because he was willing to put into practice Benjamin Franklin's admonition that a good workman should know how to saw with a file and to file with a saw. For those who believe that science can prosper only through the lavish working facilities provided in the modern research institutions, there is a lesson in the fact that the earliest of the great research institutes, the Pasteur Institute in Paris, did not open its doors until 1888, when Pasteur's own working days were over!

A Single Gigantic Problem

Pasteur's return to Paris marks the beginning of an era of incredible activity. From 1857 until 1888 his notebooks and publications reveal a multitude of projects—including theoretical studies, practical applications, and passionate debates—all carried out more or less simultaneously. All his activities were so intermingled that it would be impossible to continue their account along chronological lines. For the sake of convenience, we shall therefore postpone until the end of this book most of the facts concerning Pasteur's activities as a philosopher of science, a citizen, and a controversionalist. His investigative work can conveniently be divided into two periods separated by the year 1877. From that year on, he devoted most of his energy to the study of animal and human diseases. The scientific activities of the period 1857–77 can be considered under several separate scientific headings, but it must be emphasized again that these headings are arbitrary and justified only by reasons of convenience in presentation. In reality, the subjects that will be discussed in the following pages do not constitute unrelated topics, but rather the multiple facets of a single gigantic problem that Pasteur studied with passion and almost without interruption for a period of twenty years.

Chapter 6

Spontaneous Generation

Let us start with a problem that was not the first Pasteur undertook after his return to Paris, but certainly was in his mind from the beginning of his studies with microorganisms. If, as he believed, the souring of milk, the alcoholic fermentation of beet juice, the conversion of grape juice into wine, the conversion of wine into vinegar, the putrefaction of meat, and so many other dramatic changes in organic matter, were really caused by microbial action, where did the microorganisms responsible for these changes originate? Were they generated *de novo* in milk, beet juice, grape juice, wine, meat, etc., etc., or did they already exist somewhere ready to start their activities as soon as conditions proved favorable for them? This question was not original with Pasteur; it had been debated by philosophers and experimenters for more than twenty centuries. But it was a very exciting question, raising as it did the problem of the origin of life. Those who believed that microorganisms could arise *de novo* without parents, in fermenting or putrefying materials, did in fact accept that life was continually being created anew from inanimate matter. This belief came to be known as the doctrine of spontaneous generation. In contrast, many scientists and philosophers denied this possibility and asserted that every living thing arises from living things with similar characteristics. The faith of those who denied that spontaneous generation ever occurred was summarized in the Latin dictum: *"Omnis cellula e cellula"* (only from cells arise cells).

We shall not review here all the facts and reasons, or rather pseudo facts and pseudo reasons, which had accumulated on both sides of the debate over the preceding centuries. Let it merely be mentioned that before Pasteur entered the arena, the attitude of reasonable, unprejudiced persons was uncertain, or evenly divided between the two parties. After Pasteur had done his work, there was no longer any reason to believe that spontaneous generation ever occurs—under ordinary conditions at least. This clarification of the age-old controversy is the best possible evidence not only of Pasteur's skill as an experimenter and as a theoretical scientist, but also of the uniqueness of his contributions to this field.

There is no way at the present time of judging whether Pasteur undertook this problem with any prejudiced view. Time and time again, he asserted that he was ready to believe in spontaneous generation if it could be shown to occur, and indeed he did try many different ways to provide conditions under which it had a chance to occur. But all was in vain. Never did any growth of any sort develop when all precautions had been taken to keep out the microorganisms that he assumed to be in the surrounding air or on nearby objects. But the precautions that had to be taken were infinite, and earlier investigators who thought they had observed spontaneous generation had not been aware of these difficulties. This was where Pasteur revealed in the most spectacular manner his resourcefulness as an experimenter.

Grapes with and without Yeasts

It would take a long volume to describe the many different kinds of experiments that he performed while dealing with the problem of spontaneous generation. A spectacular one was to remove with a fine needle the juice from grapes with undamaged skin, and to show that if this was done with all precautions necessary to avoid contact with air or objects, the juice did not ferment until yeast had been added to it. This experiment he repeated late in 1878 in a modified and much extended form to counteract new claims by the famous French scientist Claude Bernard, who suggested that the spontaneous generation of yeast was possible after all. In addition to its scientific interest, this episode has the merit of illustrating Pasteur's working methods, his ardor in returning to already conquered positions when they were threatened, and the suddenness with which he took decisions when he judged that an important issue was at stake. "Without too much care for expense," he wrote, "I ordered in all haste several hothouses with the intention of transporting them to the Jura, where I possess a vineyard some dozens of square meters in size. There was not a moment to lose. And this is why.

"I have shown . . . that the germs of yeast are not yet present on the grape . . . at the end of July. . . . By taking this moment to cover some vine with hothouses almost hermetically closed, I could have, in October at grape harvest time, vines bearing ripe grapes without any yeasts on the surface. These grapes, being crushed with the precautions necessary to exclude yeast from the air, should not be able to ferment or to make wine.

"The fourth of August, 1878, my hothouses were finished and ready to be installed. . . . During and after their installation, I searched with care to see if yeasts were really absent from the clusters. . . . The result was what I expected . . . the vines covered by the hothouses bore no trace of yeast. . . .

"Toward the tenth of October, the grapes in the hothouses were ripe; one could clearly distinguish the seeds through their skin and they were as sweet in taste as the majority of the grapes grown outside. . . .

"On the tenth of October, I made my first experiment on the grapes of the uncovered clusters. . . . The result, I may say, surpassed my expectation. . . . Today, after a multitude of trials, I am just where I started, that is to say, it has been impossible for me to obtain one *single time* the alcoholic yeast fermentation from clusters protected with cotton.

"A comparative experiment naturally suggested itself. . . . It was to be expected that if I exposed hothouse clusters in the open . . . they would now ferment under the influence of the yeasts which they could not fail to receive in their new location. This was precisely the result that I obtained."

The Swan-neck Flask

Among the many other types of experiments that Pasteur designed to rule out spontaneous generation, one is worth some emphasis by virtue of its very simplicity and decisiveness and because it finally silenced his opponents and settled the issue —at least for the time being. A fermentable fluid was put into a flask, the long neck of which was then heated and drawn into the form of an S tube (hence the name "swan-neck flask"). When the liquid was boiled, the vapor forced the air out through the orifice of the neck. As the fluid became cool again, the air slowly returned to the flask, but was washed in the moisture that condensed in the curves of the neck after heating was interrupted. Under these conditions, any dust or particle carried by the air was trapped in the neck, and the fluid in the flask remained clear, sterile. However, when the neck of the flask was broken, and the unwashed air allowed to come into contact with the fluid, then microscopic life immediately began to develop.

Despite the spectacular success of these experiments, there were still unforeseen difficulties to overcome. They arose from the fact, then unknown but now well understood, that certain species of bacteria form heat-resistant spores. In some of the early experiments these spores persisted in the fluid that was presumed to have been sterilized by heating, and when they germinated, they gave rise to bacterial growth even though access to outside air had been prevented. These difficulties arising from the presence of heat-resistant spores were eventually overcome, and Pasteur was able to prepare his swan-neck flasks in such a manner that the broth remained sterile in them all. Some of these flasks prepared almost 100 years ago can still be seen today at the Pasteur Institute in Paris, the fluid as limpid as the day it was sterilized.

Pasteur was careful to emphasize over and over again that his experiments did not deal with the problem of the origin of life, but merely with the fact that microorganisms do not generate *de novo* in sterile broth or in other organic materials. Nevertheless, for years studies of spontaneous generation were carried out in an atmosphere of intense excitement and of passionate controversy because it was erroneously thought by some of the participants that the problem involved religious issues— a view which Pasteur denied strenuously. One of the high points of the debate was a lecture that

Pasteur delivered in 1864 at one of the "scientific evenings" of the Sorbonne. Before a brilliant public, which included celebrities in addition to professors and students, Pasteur outlined the historical background of the controversy, the technical aspects of his experiments, their significance, and their limitations. Presenting to his audience the swan-neck flasks in which heated infusions had remained sterile in contact with natural air, he formulated his conclusion in these words of singular beauty:

"And, therefore, gentlemen, I could point to that liquid and say to you, I have taken my drop of water from the immensity of creation, and I have taken it full of the elements appropriated to the development of microscopic organisms. And I wait, I watch, I question it!—begging it to recommence for me the beautiful spectacle of the first creation. But it is dumb, dumb since these experiments were begun several years ago; it is dumb because I have kept it from the only thing man does not know how to produce: from the germs which float in the air, from Life, for Life is a germ and a germ is Life. Never will the doctrine of spontaneous generation recover from the mortal blow of this simple experiment."

The Germ Theory

It has not recovered yet; it may never. Today, after almost a century, the fluids in these very same flasks stand unaltered, witness to the fact that man can protect organic matter from the destructive action of living forces, but has not yet learned the secret of organizing matter into Life.

However, it must be emphasized that what had been settled was not a theory of the origin of life. Nothing had been learned of the conditions under which Life had first appeared, and no one knows even today whether it is still emerging anew from inanimate matter. The fact that had been established was that microbial life would not appear in an organic medium that had been adequately sterilized, and subsequently protected from outside contamination. The germ theory is not a philosophical theory of life, but merely a body of factual observations from a series of practical operations. It teaches that fermentation, decomposition, putrefaction are caused by living microorganisms, ubiquitous in nature; that these microorganisms are not begotten by the decomposing or fermenting fluid, but come into it from the outside; that sterile liquid exposed to sterile air will remain sterile forever.

It was this concept that Pasteur expounded in his Sorbonne lecture before an amphitheater overflowing with a fashionable audience that had come expecting to hear a statement concerning the origin, nature, and meaning of life. But wisely he refrained from philosophizing. He did not deny that spontaneous generation was a possibility; he merely affirmed that it had never been shown to occur. The words he pronounced on that occasion constitute the permanent rock on which were built whole sections of biological sciences: "There is no known circumstance in which it has been shown that microscopic beings come into the world without germs, without parents similar to themselves. Those who affirm it have been duped by illusions, by ill-conducted experiments, by errors that they either did not perceive, or did not know how to avoid."

Interestingly enough, there is at the present time a renewal of interest in the origin of life. On the one hand, many efforts are being made to imagine types of chemical reactions that would be self-reproducing and thus exhibit one of the most distinctive properties of life. On the other hand, the discovery that certain viruses can be crystallized and are amenable to chemical analysis has fostered the hope that we might be getting close to identifying the chemical structures characteristic of living processes. Only time will tell to what extent these efforts really bear on the perennial problem of the origin of life, a problem which constitutes one of the common grounds of science and philosophy. But what is certain is that none of the present developments conflicts in any way with the conclusions of Pasteur's work on spontaneous generation. It can be said, in fact, that no constructive thinking on the problem of the origin of life was possible until the ghost of spontaneous generation had been slain. Science may eventually show that there is something fundamentally true in the ancient notion that life may have arisen from a kind of primeval ooze. But certainly microbes do not arise *de novo* from fermenting fluids nor from putrefying meat, and in this limited sense Pasteur was absolutely right. Never will the doctrine of spontaneous generation recover from the mortal blow of his beautiful experiments!

The New Science of Bacteriology

In addition to settling the controversy on spontaneous generation, Pasteur's efforts served to establish the new science of bacteriology on a solid technical basis. Exacting procedures had to be devised to prevent the introduction of germs from the outside into the system under study, and also to destroy germs already present in it. Because of this necessity, the fundamental techniques of aseptic manipulation and of sterilization were worked out between 1860 and 1880. Incidental to the controversy also, there were discovered many facts concerning the distribution of microorganisms in our surroundings, in air and in water. It was also found that the blood and urine of normal animals and of man are free from microbes and can be preserved without exhibiting putrefying changes if collected with suitable aseptic precautions. All these observations constitute the concrete basis on which was eventually erected our understanding of the natural history of microbial life. Moreover, as we shall see, Pasteur derived from his studies of spontaneous generation the germ theory of disease and many of the laws of epidemiology.

The controversy on spontaneous generation was the exacting school at which bacteriology became aware of its problems and learned its methodology.

Chapter 7

Pasteurization

The demonstration that microbes do not generate spontaneously encouraged the development of techniques to destroy them and to prevent or minimize subsequent contamination. Immediately these advances brought about profound technological changes in the preparation and preservation of food products and subsequently in other industrial processes as well.

Pasteur's awareness of the fact that microorganisms can interfere with biological processes arose from his early experiences with alcoholic fermentation in Lille. He had then noticed that typical yeast globules were the only structures seen under the microscope when the fermentation was healthy, whereas smaller microscopic forms became prevalent when fermentation was defective. While on vacation in his country home at Arbois, in September 1858, he had occasion to submit some spoiled wines to microscopic examination and saw in them microorganisms similar in shape to the lactic-acid bacteria which he had just discovered. This observation, and his experience in the Lille distillery, probably led him to conclude that the "diseases" of fermentations were caused by microorganisms which competed with yeast in the fermenting fluid. His studies of vinegar production provided further evidence for this view.

Wine, Vinegar, and Beer

Souring is one of the most common types of deterioration affecting wine; and Pasteur soon discovered that this change resulted from the oxidation of alcohol to acetic acid by a process similar to or identical with that carried out by the bacteria *Mycoderma aceti* for the transformation of wine into vinegar. In addition to souring, there are many other types of alternations that unfavorably affect the quality of wines; the Bordeaux wines "turn," the Burgundy wines become "bitter," the Champagnes become "ropy." Fortunately, Pasteur was well placed to test by experimentation his general thesis that these "diseases" also came from contamination by foreign organisms, for some of his childhood friends owned well-stocked cellars at Arbois. There, in an improvised laboratory, he examined systematically under the microscope all the healthy and diseased wines that were submitted to him. From the very beginning success rewarded his efforts, for whenever a sample had been found defective in some respect, he discovered, mingled with the yeast cells, other distinct microscopic forms. So skillful did he become in the detection of these various germs that he soon was able to predict the particular flavor of a wine from an examination of the sediment. In "healthy" wines the foreign bodies were absent and yeast cells alone were to be seen. More or less simultaneously, he made similar observations with regard to vinegar manufacture, finding that here again defects in the quality of the product could be related to the presence of microorganisms other than *Mycoderma aceti.*

Like wine and vinegar, beer was often found to undergo spontaneous alterations, to become acid, and even putrid, especially in the summer. Pasteur demonstrated that these alterations were always caused by microscopic organisms, and he described his findings in a book published in 1877 under the title *Etudes sur la bière, ses maladies, les causes qui les provoquent. Procédés pour la rendre inaltérable, avec une théorie nouvelle de la fermentation.* He had taken up the study of brewing techniques after the Franco-Prussian War of 1870–71, in a pathetic attempt to enhance French prestige by improving the quality of French beer and thus surpassing Germany in one of her most famous products. These studies, carried out in Pasteur's own laboratory converted for a while into a pilot brewery, and also at the Wilbread brewery in London, led to the conclusion that, as in wine, the defects that occur "in the wort, and in the beer itself, are due to the presence of microscopic organisms of a nature totally different from those belonging to the yeast proper. . . .

"As all the disease germs of wort and beer are destroyed in the copper vessels in which the wort is heated, and as the introduction of pure yeast from a pure beer cannot introduce in the latter any ferment of a detrimental nature, it follows that it ought to be possible to prepare beers incapable of developing any mischievous foreign ferments whatever. This can be done provided that the wort coming from the copper vessels is protected from ordinary air . . . and fermented with pure yeast, and that the beer is placed in vessels carefully freed from ferments at the end of fermentation."

It was soon discovered that the introduction of microorganisms in biological products can be minimized by an intelligent and rigorous control of the technological operations, but cannot be prevented entirely. The problem therefore was to inhibit the further development of these organisms after they had been introduced into the product. To this end, Pasteur first tried to add a variety of antiseptics, but the results were mediocre and, after much hesitation, he considered the possibility of using heat as a sterilizing agent.

Partial Sterilization or "Pasteurization"

His first studies of heat as a preserving agent were carried out with wine. As will be recalled, he had grown up in one of the best wine districts in France, and, as a connoisseur of the beverage, was much disturbed at the thought that heating might alter its flavor and bouquet. He therefore proceeded with very great caution and eventually convinced himself that heating at 55° C. would not alter appreciably the bouquet of wine if the treatment was applied only after the oxygen originally present in the bottle had become exhausted. These considerations led to the process of partial sterilization, which soon became known the world over under the name of "pasteurization," and which was found applicable to wine, beer, cider, vinegar, milk, and countless other perishable beverages, foods, and organic products.

It was characteristic of Pasteur that he did not remain satisfied with formulating the theoretical basis of heat sterilization, but took an active interest in designing industrial equipment adapted to the heating of fluids in large volumes and at low cost. His treatises on vinegar, wine, and beer are illustrated with drawings and photographs of this type of equipment, and describe in detail the operations involved in the process. The word "pasteurization" is, indeed, a symbol of his scientific life; it recalls the part he played in establishing the theoretical basis of the germ theory, and the phenomenal effort that he devoted to making it useful to his fellow men. It reminds us also of his well-known statement: "There are no such things as pure and applied science—there are only science, and the applications of science."

While it is of no scientific interest, it might be worth mentioning an incident that bears on a point of ethics of increasing relevance to the behavior of university scientists in modern industrial societies. Pasteur was not a wealthy man, and there is no doubt that his family responsibilities often weighed on his mind. It is known that after he had developed techniques for the preservation of vinegar, wine, and beer with the use of heat, he took patents to protect the rights to his discovery. That there were discussions within his family concerning the possible financial exploitation of these patents is revealed in one of his letters: "My wife . . . who worries concerning the future of our children, gives me good reasons for overcoming my scruples." Nevertheless, he decided to release his patents to the public, and he did not derive financial profit even from the development or sale of large-scale industrial equipment devised for pasteurization.

For American readers, it will be of interest to learn that pasteurization was immediately adopted in the United States, even in far-away and as yet undeveloped California. Pasteur took great pride in this recognition of his work so far away from France, and he stated in one of his articles: "It is inspiring to hear from the citizen of a country where the grapevine did not exist twenty years ago, that, to credit a French discovery, he has experimented at one stroke on 100,000 liters of wine. These men go forward with giant steps, while we timidly place one foot in front of the other. . . ."

New Understanding of Ancient Practices

Pasteurization was not, of course, the first practical technique devised by man for the preservation of foodstuffs. In fact, many other techniques had been developed empirically in the past throughout the world, and are still being used today. Thus, sun-drying, or desiccation, has been a practice from time immemorial for the preservation of strips of meat and of some fruit in subtropical countries. The smoke used in curing meat possesses antiseptic properties which prevent or at least retard putrefaction, and to a certain extent this is probably true of some of the spices commonly added to foodstuffs. The high concentration of salt in brine also acts as inhibitor of bacterial growth as does the acetic acid of vinegar in pickled products and the lactic acid in sauerkraut. Until Pasteur's time, the most effective method of food preservation had been the controlled heating introduced by Appert around 1810, a forerunner of the practices used at the present time in the canning industry. It is of interest to note in passing that, at the time of the controversies on spontaneous generation, soups, meats, vegetables, and fruit had been canned on an extensive scale for fifty years by Appert's method, so that it may seem that Pasteur was demonstrating the obvious. But there is always a lag in many scientists' apprehension of the implications of the practical man's work. One could say facetiously that Pasteur had to demonstrate to scientists what the housewife already knew.

All the examples mentioned show how much had been discovered by trial and error long before the days of experimental science. What Pasteur brought to the problem was the concept that most food spoilage is caused by microorganisms of various kinds, and he thus provided a new understanding that gave increased significance to the ancient empirical techniques. Scientific knowledge permitted rapid improvements with entirely new techniques.

Although less than one century has elapsed since Pasteur introduced the scientific approach to the preservation of foodstuffs, more progress has been made in that relatively short time than had been accomplished through millennia of trial and error! Such is the superiority of experimental science over empiricism! There is no doubt, moreover, that further progress is in the offing. Heating (pasteurization) is only one of the techniques that can destroy or inhibit microorganisms. It is quite satisfactory for the preservation of milk, beverages, and for the canning of certain other foodstuffs, but it has limitations with regard to more delicate products. Very recently preservation of foodstuffs by radiation has come under consideration, and even though its use in foodstuffs has not yet been sanctioned, it is possible that radiation eventually will find a place in food sterilization and other technological procedures. Progress is now rapid, because it is no longer empirical. Ever since Pasteur, the problems of food spoilage have been well defined. Much is known of the microorganisms that have to be dealt with in each particular situation, and it is therefore possible to plan technological procedures in such a way that they achieve the desired end with the least amount of alteration in the food product.

Chapter 8

Utilizing Microbes

Pasteurization with its subsequent developments was only one of the many technological applications that followed from Pasteur's discoveries. Other and even more important practical consequences grew out of his demonstration that microorganisms of all sorts play a dominant role in the changes that organic matter endlessly undergoes in nature. In 1867, in a letter written to an important French public official, he outlined his views regarding the power of microbial life:

"We know that the substances extracted from plants ferment when they are abandoned to themselves, and disappear little by little in contact with the air. We know that the cadavers of animals undergo putrefaction and that soon only their skeletons remain. This destruction of dead organic matter is one of the necessities of the perpetuation of life.

"If the remnants of dead plants and animals were not destroyed, the surface of the earth would soon be encumbered with organic matter, and life would become impossible because the cycle of transformation . . . could no longer be closed.

"It is necessary that the fibrin of our muscles, the albumin of our blood, the gelatin of our bones, the urea of our urine, the ligneous matter of plants, the sugar of their fruits, the starch of their seeds . . . be progressively converted into water, ammonia and carbon dioxide so that the elementary principles of these complex organic substances be taken up again by plants, elaborated anew, to serve as food for new living beings similar to those that gave birth to them, and so on *ad infinitum* to the end of the centuries."

The Indispensable Links

Without denying that ordinary chemical forces can slowly attack organic matter, Pasteur thus affirmed his belief that decomposition is chiefly caused by microorganisms. And indeed, it is now realized that substances of animal or plant origin undergo sooner or later a chain of chemical alterations which break them down, step by step, into simpler and simpler compounds, and that in this fashion the chemical elements are returned to nature after death for the support of new life. "All are of the dust, and all turn to dust again." It was one of Pasteur's greatest achievements to show that all the structures and products of plants, animals, and other forms of life eventually become food for countless types of microorganisms, which in an orderly progressive manner make use of them for building their own bodies and which in their turn die to make these materials available for other forms of life. Microorganisms constitute, therefore, indispensable links in the eternal chain that binds life to inanimate matter.

Pasteur foresaw, and it is now known as a fact, that soil harbors huge numbers of microorganisms of all sorts which endlessly transform organic matter, while others play a similar role with regard to the nitrogen of the air and the minerals of the rocks. The immense amounts of refuse that find their way into sewage are broken down by microorganisms and thus can be more readily utilized, or disposed of. There is no end to the list that could be made of the activities of microorganisms in the economy of nature—whether they be the rusting of iron pipes, the genesis of petroleum, or the decomposition of leaves on the forest floor. Truly as Pasteur was wont to say, "The role of the infinitely small in nature is infinitely great."

The Benefits of Precise Knowledge

Since for almost every type of substance there exists in nature some microorganism peculiarly adapted to its destruction or modification, it follows that man should be able to take advantage of this diversity and versatility of the microbial world for purposes useful to him. In fact, from time immemorial and all over the world, microorganisms have been used empirically in many varied technological processes. We have mentioned several times in preceding pages the production of wine, of beer, of vinegar, and of sour milk, but these fermentations constitute only a few examples among the ancient processes in which microbes take a part—all the way from cheese making to the retting of flax, from the preparation of cocoa beans to the ripening of clay. Here again, Pasteur's contribution was to show how procedures devised in the past by trial and error could be improved through precise knowledge of the microbes and of their chemical activities. Although he applied this understanding chiefly to the production of wine, vinegar, and beer, he saw much further than these limited applications would indicate. Realizing that microorganisms can be adapted to the performance of almost any kind of biochemical reaction, he was bold enough to state: "A day will come, I am convinced, when microorganisms will be utilized in certain industrial operations on account of their ability to transform organic matter." This prophecy has been fulfilled, and today organic acids, various solvents, vitamins, drugs, and enzymes are produced on an enormous scale by microbial processes—all this a logical development of Pasteur's work.

For example, the commercial production of lactic acid and of citric acid began around the turn of the century. Butanol and acetone, as well as glycerol, were produced on a large scale by fermentation during the First World War. The first commercial production of gluconic acid and of riboflavin dates from 1938, and by now other vitamins are also produced totally or partially by microbial fermentation. In recent years public attention has been focused on the industrial production of anti-bacterial drugs by microorganisms—penicillin being the most famous of the so-called antibiotics. But these are not the only drugs of microbial origin; ergot, for example, is a product of the fungus *Claviceps purpurea*, which has great importance in medical practice. Among other chemicals of industrial importance produced by various types of microorganisms, one should also mention many types of enzymes—diastases, proteases, pectases—which are used widely in food products and in a great variety of industrial processes.

Amino acids constitute a new group of microbial products related to nutrition, which looms very large in importance. Plant proteins from seeds and tubers are often deficient in the amino acids methionine, lysine, tryptophan, threonine, and proline, and for this reason have a low nutritional value. A cheap source of amino acids would therefore be of enormous importance for supplementing animal feeds, and also for improving human nutrition, especially in the underprivileged parts of the world. Present research in a number of laboratories is being directed toward the production of essential amino acids by fermentation. In theory, it should be possible, by the judicious selection of microbial strains, to produce almost any amino acid with the help of microorganisms. In practice, of course, many difficulties arise. Nevertheless, a

78

process for microbial production of lysine has been worked out, and work is reported to be well advanced with regard to the production of glutamic acid and tryptophan.

As a last example of industrial microbiology, I shall mention the large-scale production of yeast cells, a subject very closely related to Pasteur's early scientific interests. In addition to its practical importance, this industry provides a wonderful illustration of the influence that theoretical studies exert on technological processes. Pasteur had shown that when yeast is grown in the absence of oxygen, there results a wasteful utilization of sugar with accumulation of alcohol. This is, of course, a desirable result in the production of wine, beer, and in other fermentations in which alcohol is the desired product. But the yield of yeast cells is very small during alcoholic fermentation in the absence of oxygen. In contrast, hardly any alcohol is produced from sugar when oxygen is readily available, and the yield of yeast cells is then very large. For this reason, the yeast grower always provides intense aeration of the culture medium whenever his aim is to produce yeast cells to be used in the baking industry, in the home, or as a source of food.

Thus, Pasteur demonstrated that with the proper knowledge one could control the biochemical activities of microorganisms, and make them produce almost any type of chemical compound, the most complicated as well as the simplest. Thousands of years ago, man had learned to domesticate certain plants and animals, and he has continued to use these on his farms or in his home in much the same way as did his ancestors. It can be said that the domestication of microbial life entered the scientific era with Pasteur, and that, thanks to him, microbial industries reached within two generations a very high level of diversification and of efficiency.

Chapter 9

Biochemistry and Life

We must now go back to the year 1857 and watch in more detail Pasteur's early struggles with the problems of alcoholic and lactic-acid fermentation. The first task he assumed after returning to the Ecole Normale was to prove beyond doubt that yeast and the lactic-acid ferment were really living things. It is not easy for us to realize the skepticism, indeed the hostility, which prevailed at that time in the scientific world against the view that microscopic living creatures could perform important chemical reactions. The extent of the scorn that scientists professed for this view appears in a skit published by Friedrich Wöhler—the famous chemist who had first synthesized urea—in the journal *Annalen der Chemie*. In this sarcastic document Wöhler described yeast with a considerable degree of anatomical realism, as consisting of eggs which developed into minute animals shaped like distilling apparatus. These creatures took in sugar as food and digested it into carbonic acid and alcohol, which were separately excreted. The famous chemist and biologist, Justus von Liebig, dismissed the germ theory with a shrug of the shoulders, regarding Pasteur's view that microbes could cause fermentation as ridiculous and naïve as the opinion of a child "who would explain the rapidity of the Rhine current by attributing it to the violent movement of the many millwheels at Maintz."

Pasteur Persists

Fortunately, Pasteur was not intimidated by the haughty scorn of his scientific elders, and he countered their heavy witticism with an experiment of incredible simplicity and elegance. It turned out to have an enormous influence on the subsequent history of biochemical sciences. Very boldly he undertook to grow yeast in a simple medium devoid of complex organic nitrogenous compounds—a liquid containing only sugar, ammonia, and some mineral salts to supply the yeast globules with their structural elements. He had the ingenious idea of adding to his nutrient medium the ashes of incinerated yeast in addition to the salts of phosphoric acid, potassium, magnesium, and iron, hoping to supply thereby the unknown mineral elements required by the small plant. He acknowledged that, under these conditions, yeast grew less readily than it did in the juice of the grape or in beer brew, probably because it had to synthesize all its tissue constituents instead of finding many of the metabolic factors ready-made in the natural organic fluids. Nevertheless, he could report in 1860 that he had obtained fermentation in his synthetic medium inoculated with minute amounts of yeast, and that the amount of alcohol produced ran parallel with the multiplication of the yeast. With less refinement, but a like method, he applied similar techniques to lactic-acid fermentation and then to other reactions that he proved were the results of microbial activities. Of all these studies we shall mention only two that illustrate the breadth of his understanding of biochemical phenomena.

It had long been known that the production of vinegar from wine, as in the French Orleans process, or from dilute alcohol as practiced in Germany, was essentially the result of an oxidation converting the alcohol into acetic acid. In the French process oxidation was favored by exposing the wine to the air in very shallow layers; in the German process by making the dilute alcohol trickle down over wood shavings so as to secure intense aeration. It was also known that this oxidation was "catalyzed" by the presence of a slimy organic material called "mother of vinegar." Here again, as with yeast, Pasteur established that when minute amounts of the mother of vinegar were transferred to a synthetic solution containing dilute alcohol, ammonia, and mineral salts, the slimy material increased in abundance, and simultaneously produced acetic acid. He saw under the microscope that the whole process was accompanied by the multiplication of minute bacteria which adhered together to form the mother of vinegar, and he even recognized the presence of the bacteria on the surface of acidifying wine or on the wood shavings used in the German process. This understanding led to rapid improvements in the processes of vinegar production, and moreover, it greatly enlarged understanding of the chemical potentialities of microorganisms.

The Discovery of "Anaerobic" Life

Even more thought-provoking was the unexpected discovery that certain types of bacteria could live without air. According to Pasteur's account, he had once placed under the microscope a drop of sugar solution that was in the process of changing into butyric acid. The drop contained bacteria, which were at first rapidly motile. Then he observed the odd fact that whereas the bacteria in the center of the drop continued to move, those at the periphery soon came to a standstill. From this simple observation he guessed that air was toxic for these bacteria and that they probably lived without oxygen. Accurate as it is, this account gives only a very incomplete picture of what had happened in Pasteur's mind as he was looking at the drop of fluid under the microscope. He had repeatedly observed that butyric acid was more likely to appear in sugar solutions that were either kept free of air altogether, or at least poorly aerated. Subconsciously in other words, his mind had stored facts that were compatible with the view that butyric fermentation did take place in the absence of oxygen, and what he saw under the microscope immediately acquired meaning in the light of these subconscious thoughts. Once again, chance had favored him, but only because many days of observation and thought had prepared him and made him receptive to the new findings. There was no precedent for the view that life could occur in the absence of oxygen; in fact, this view went against all accepted notions. Yet, not only did Pasteur recognize this possibility, but he immediately incorporated it in his thinking and without further ado soon coined the adjective "anaerobic" to refer to life without oxygen, in contrast to "aerobic" for life as usually known in the presence of air.

As pointed out before, it is unfortunate that all these discoveries of Pasteur must be stated individually, for they did not occur as separate events, as well-defined experiments planned today, carried out tomorrow, and written up immediately. In reality all the aspects of this work on fermentations were continuously reacting one with the other, influencing each other, giving new significance to old observations and leading to new hypotheses. In an attempt to co-ordinate the multiple factors of this extraordinary intellectual feat and so give it some sort of unity, we shall state briefly here some of the general conclusions Pasteur had reached when he came to the end of this phase of his activities. The most complete statement of his views in this field is found in his book on beer, published in 1876. The circumstances were sufficiently odd to warrant a few words at this point.

It will be recalled that Pasteur came from one of the parts of France famous for good wine and that he worked on the improvement of beer manufacture after the Franco-Prussian War of 1870–71, merely as a way of advancing French competition with Germany in the economic and gustatory field! On reading his book, one gets the impression that he found relief from working on a subject that he disliked—beer—by thinking about a problem in which he was deeply interested—the nature of fermentation. Thus did it come about that the book on beer gave him the opportunity to summarize much of the biochemical wisdom and understanding he had derived from his earlier studies on fermentation.

Let us go back to the various types of microbial activity that Pasteur had studied in greatest detail. One, the production of acetic acid, involved the use of large amounts of oxygen for the oxidation of alcohol. In contrast, the conversion of sugar into butyric acid corresponded to a chemical reduction in which oxygen did not intervene and did in fact inhibit the activity of the butyric-acid ferment. The lactic-acid fermentation corresponded to still another type of reaction which occurred more or less independently of oxygen through an apparently simple splitting of one glucose molecule into two molecules of lactic acid. At first sight, it seemed that each and every one of these microbial activities constituted a phenomenon completely apart from the other, not having anything in common. However, Pasteur came to an entirely different conclusion, in large part, it would seem, on the basis of his profound and original studies of the life of yeast.

Point of Synthesis: The Utilization of Oxygen

The great advantage of yeast for these studies was that it can grow both in the absence and in the presence of air. Moreover, and this turned out to be the key to the whole problem, the mode of growth of yeast is very different depending upon the intensity of aeration during its contact with sugar. Yeast grows slowly and fermentation takes a long time in the complete absence of air, but the amount of sugar transformed into carbon dioxide and alcohol per unit of yeast is then extremely high. For example, 0.5–0.7 gm. (grams) of yeast was sufficient in Pasteur's experiments to transform 100 gm. of sugar into alcohol in the absence of air, a ratio of 1 to 150 or 1 to 200. On the other hand, as the amount of air admitted during fermentation is increased, the development of yeast becomes more rapid and more abundant, and the ratio of weight of sugar fermented to weight of yeast becomes smaller. When an excess of oxygen is provided throughout the process, hardly any alcohol is formed, although the development of yeast is very abundant and the ratio of sugar consumed to yeast produced falls to approximately 5. Some alteration of the morphological characteristics of the yeast also occurs simultaneously with these dramatic changes in physiological behavior.

These extraordinary differences in the chemical behavior of yeast depending upon the availability of oxygen led Pasteur to postulate that living cells can obtain energy from foodstuffs through two very different types of mechanisms. One involves utilization of oxygen and is very effective because the complete oxidation of foodstuffs with little waste product releases a great deal of energy, most of which becomes available to the cell. Another mechanism occurs without oxygen, but is very wasteful. For example, the conversion of sugar into lactic acid, alcohol, or butyric acid provides the cell with chemical energy but only in very small amounts. The process is wasteful because lactic acid, butyric acid, or alcohol can be regarded as waste products that the particular bacterium or yeast cannot utilize because it cannot oxidize it. The fact that these waste products happen to be useful to man is, of course, another story. Yeast proved to be the best organism for the analysis of this problem: it can live aerobically with an effective utilization of sugar for energy production through almost complete oxidation by means of oxygen, or it can live anaerobically with a wasteful utilization of sugar, leaving alcohol as an unoxidized by-product. In brief, fermentation was the method used by yeast to derive energy from sugar under anaerobic conditions. In 1872 Pasteur restated these views in more precise terms: "Under ordinary conditions, the heat (energy) necessary for development comes from the oxidation of foodstuffs (except in the case of utilization of solar light). In fermentation, it comes from the decomposition of the fermentable matter. The ratio of the weight of fermentable matter decomposed to the weight of yeast produced will be higher or lower depending upon the extent of action of free oxygen. The maximum will correspond to life with participation of free oxygen."

A *Definition of Fermentation*

Eventually, Pasteur summarized his understanding of these complex phenomena in a few arresting formulae, the gist of which is that "fermentation is respiration in the absence of air." Moreover, he recognized that what he had observed was not peculiar to yeast and bacteria, but was instead a phenomenon of great generality. For example, he noticed that, while plums kept in an open container took up oxygen and became soft and sweet, they remained firm, lost sugar, and produced alcohol if placed in an atmosphere of carbon dioxide. Time and time again he restated his belief that: "Fermentation should be possible in all types of cells. . . . Fermentation by yeast is only a particular case of a very general phenomenon. All living beings are ferments under certain conditions of their life. . . ."

Specifically he suggested that the same principles apply also to animal tissues, for example, to muscle. And in fact it is now well established that muscle cells, and probably all animal tissue cells, can derive some energy from the conversion of sugar into lactic acid, just as bacteria do. But this is a very wasteful process, and, moreover, its outcome is the accumulation of lactic acid which soon proves to have toxic effects. In normal life, therefore, the production of energy is rendered much more economical and efficient, and the accumulation of toxic products prevented, by the respiratory mechanisms which bring oxygen into the reaction to complete oxidative processes. Thus did Pasteur elevate some specialized observations on microbial activities to the level of one of the most fundamental biochemical laws of life.

The Chemical Mystery of Life

The detailed study of yeast led Pasteur to still another broad biological generalization. He had shown that yeast could be grown in a simple broth containing sugar and mineral salts as its main constituents. Likewise, he succeeded in cultivating in well-defined culture media many other types of bacteria. His first graduate student at the Ecole Normale, Raulin, greatly advanced the knowledge of microbial nutrition by working out the requirements of a mold, *Aspergillus niger*, and showing in particular that certain metals and other rare mineral elements are required for its normal growth. As early as 1860 Pasteur himself pointed out that these findings made in his laboratory would permit physiology to attack the fundamental chemical problems of life. The bodies of plants and animals consist of an immense number of cells, but in microorganisms the living agent is reduced to the single-cell level. By studying microbial physiology, therefore, it is possible to analyze the chemical phenomena which determine the function of the individual cell—the fundamental unit of life—be it that of a plant, a microorganism, an animal, or even a man. In practice it is today possible to grow *in vitro* (in test tubes) almost every kind of living cell and thus to define its particular requirements. And this general technique has revealed the fascinating fact that living cells possess many characteristics in common. For example, it is now known that most vitamins intervene in the metabolism of all cells. The fact that some cells require and others do not require a particular vitamin for growth is of little importance in this respect, because those that do not require the vitamin manufacture it themselves and use it just as the others do in the course of their biochemical living processes.

Thus, it can be said that Pasteur's work led inescapably to the doctrine of the biochemical unity of life, truly one of the most important philosophical concepts of modern science.

While Pasteur's studies of the biological significance of stereoisomerism did not throw any light on the genesis of life, they have yielded a number of facts that have had far-reaching influence on the development of biochemistry. Pasteur himself recognized that the differences in structural configuration between the isomeric forms of tartaric acids, as well as of other organic compounds, are reflected in the differential behavior of these isomeric substances toward living agents, for example, in their effect on taste buds and in their susceptibility to attack by microorganisms. These observations have served as a starting point for a whole range of investigations of the chemical basis of biological specificity, a problem so characteristic of modern biochemistry.

But while he recognized that the fundamental metabolic and nutritional processes are common to all known forms of life, Pasteur pondered endlessly over the mechanisms whereby each living organism transmits to its progeny its unique hereditary characteristics. Once he had convinced himself—and the world—that spontaneous generation does not occur in ordinary circumstances, he came to regard the transmissibility of hereditary traits as the unique characteristic of life. As he wrote, "The mystery of life does not reside in its manifestations in adult beings, but rather and solely in the existence of the germ and of its becoming. . . . Once the germ exists, it needs only inanimate substances and proper conditions of temperature to obey the laws of its development. . . . It will then grow and manifest all the phenomena that we call 'vital,' but vital phenomena are only physical and chemical phenomena; it is the law of their succession which constitutes the unknown of life. . . ." Modern chemical genetics is only now beginning to attack this fascinating problem of such passionate interest to Pasteur.

Chapter 10

Victory over Disease

The year 1877 constitutes a landmark in the life of Pasteur and in the history of medicine. That April he published the first of his studies on anthrax—a disease of farm animals and men—and this paper bears to the germ theory of disease the same relation that his 1857 paper on lactic acid bears to the germ theory of fermentation. Before discussing in detail the facts revealed by Pasteur's studies of infection, however, we must stop to consider how it happened that he was led to devote the rest of his life to biological and medical problems, even though he was trained as a chemist and had never studied biology, let alone medicine.

First, let us make clear that while it is true that the germ theory of disease was accepted in medical circles only after 1877, the ground for acceptance had been prepared by many centuries of solid observations and shrewd thinking. Like most other scientific theories, the belief that microbes can cause disease had emerged as an abstract concept —a hunch—long before it was possible to state the facts clearly or to test them by experiment. Over many years, the theory evolved progressively from a vague awareness to the level of precise understanding.

Contagion and the Potato Blight

From time immemorial it has been known that certain diseases are catching—like colds or tuberculosis—and that others are specially prevalent in certain places—malaria in swampy regions, for example. Awareness of these facts led very early to the concept that certain diseases can be transmitted from one person to the next by contact, or can be caused by something present in the air. The history of the expression "contagious" disease symbolizes this ancient knowledge. The word contagion comes from the Latin *contagio* which means contact. Contagion, in other words, implies the transmission of disease by direct or indirect contact. There have been many hypotheses concerning transmission of disease by contact. Some physicians believed the agent to be something volatile. Thus, the Italian word malaria means "bad air" —something noxious arising from marshes and other wet places. For other physicians the transmissible causes of disease were invisible particles in suspension in the air. Minute invisible animalcules had been implicated very early, but there was no way of proving their existence. Lack of precise knowledge concerning the nature of the transmissible agents responsible for disease did not, however, prevent practical men from establishing sanitary policies to minimize contagion. During epidemics of plague, for instance, the inhabitants of the stricken cities or districts were forbidden to move into unaffected areas for fear they would spread the disease. The policy of quarantine derives its name from the fact that in Venice ships arriving from foreign lands were held in the harbor for forty days (*quarante* in Italian) before the crew or passengers could land. Pasteur knew these facts, and it is certain that he saw in them evidence for his prejudiced view that microbes were responsible for contagion.

The first direct evidence that microbes could play a part in disease was obtained around 1850. The occasion was the potato blight, a terrible scourge which devastated the potato fields all over Ireland for several years in succession. The potato blight is of enormous importance in political and economic history because more than one million people died of the famine in Ireland; the country was ruined, all sorts of diseases became rampant among farm and city people; many of those who survived were so impoverished that they had to emigrate, especially to America, and as a result of the disaster the Irish population fell from eight million to under four million. The potato blight is also important in the history of science because it contributed much to the understanding of disease causation.

Everyone knew that the spring had been cold in Ireland the year of the blight, with much rain and fog, and the conclusion was natural that the bad weather had been responsible for the disease. A few botanists pointed out, however, that the blighted potato plants had been invaded by a microscopic fungus, *Phytophthora infestans,* and they contended that this fungus was the real cause of the disaster. As we shall see later, the discussions that followed and that have continued to our day have thrown much light on the real meaning of the expression "cause of a disease." But there is no evidence that the facts discovered around 1850 by the botanists concerning the potato blight had any influence on the thinking of physicians with regard to the nature of contagious diseases of man. At that time, it was apparently difficult to recognize that there was a close analogy between the spoiling of potatoes and the diseases of mankind.

Pasteur had never heard of the invasion of the Irish potato fields by the fungus *Phytophthora infestans,* and this is unfortunate because he would have grasped the broad significance of the phenomenon for human and veterinary medicine. Nevertheless, early in his work on fermentation he had become convinced by intuition that microbes could cause disease. He stated this conviction very explicitly as early as 1857 in his preliminary paper on lactic-acid fermentation—and he continued from then on to reiterate his hypothesis in letters, articles, and lectures. For example, in the course of his studies on spontaneous generation, he wrote in 1861: "It would be interesting to carry out frequent microscopic analysis of the dust floating in the air at the different seasons, and in different localities. The understanding of the phenomena of contagion, especially during the periods of epidemic diseases, would have much to gain from such studies." And somewhat later, he came back to the same suggestion in words that were really prophetic: "In Paris, during the month of July when the fruit trade is active, there must be large numbers of yeasts floating in the air of the streets. *If fermentations were diseases, one could speak of epidemics of fermentation.*

"Can we fail to observe that the further we penetrate into the experimental study of germs, the more we perceive unexpected lights and ideas leading to the knowledge of the causes of contagious diseases! Is it not worth noting that in this vineyard . . . every particle of soil was capable of inducing alcoholic fermentation, whereas the soil of the greenhouses was inactive in this respect. And why? Because I had taken the precaution of covering this soil with glass at the proper time. The death, if I may use this expression, of a grape falling on the ground of any vineyard, is always accompanied by the multiplication on the grape of the yeast cells; in contrast, this kind of death is impossible in the corner of soil protected by my greenhouses. . . . As the yeast cells reach the grapes only at a certain time of the year, it is possible to protect them by means of a shelter placed at the proper time, just as Europe can be protected from cholera and plague by adequate quarantine measures."

Lister Acknowledges a Debt

Pasteur had been so emphatic in suggesting that contagious diseases might be related to fermentation and putrefaction that in 1864 his writings reached the Scottish surgeon Joseph Lister. Under Pasteur's influence Lister postulated that microorganisms can cause wound suppuration, just as they cause fermentation and putrefaction. For this reason, Lister suggested that microorganisms should be prevented at all costs from reaching the hands of the surgeon, his instruments, and the very air surrounding the operating field. To achieve this, Lister used a spray of phenol throughout the operations he performed, taking his lead from the fact that this substance was then employed for the treatment of sewage and excreta. Thus began the era of modern surgery. In a most generous manner Lister often acknowledged publicly his intellectual debt to Pasteur, for example in the following letter that he wrote to him from Edinburgh in February 1874:

"My Dear Sir: Allow me to beg your acceptance of a pamphlet, which I sent by the same post, containing an account of some investigations into the subject which you have done so much to elucidate, the germ theory of fermentative changes. I flatter myself that you may read with some interest what I have written on the organisms which you were the first to describe in your *Mémoire sur la fermentation appelée lactique.*

"I do not know whether the records of British Surgery ever meet your eye. If so, you will have seen from time to time notices of the antiseptic system of treatment, which I have been labouring for the last nine years to bring to perfection.

"Allow me to take this opportunity to tender you my most cordial thanks for having, by your brilliant researches, demonstrated to me the truth of the germ theory of putrefaction, and thus furnished me with the principle upon which alone the antiseptic system can be carried out. Should you at any time visit Edinburgh it would, I believe, give you sincere gratification to see at our hospital how largely mankind is being benefited by your labours.

"I need hardly add that it would afford me the highest gratification to show you how greatly surgery is indebted to you.

"Forgive the freedom with which a common love of science inspires me, and

"Believe me, with profound respect,

Yours very sincerely,

Joseph Lister."

Lister again gave generous recognition to Pasteur in the introduction to his classical paper, *On the Antiseptic Principle in the Practice of Surgery.* In his words: "When it had been shown by the researches of Pasteur that the septic property of the atmosphere depended, not on the oxygen or a gaseous constituent, but on minute organisms suspended in it, which owed their energy to their vitality, it occurred to me that decomposition in the injured part might be avoided without excluding the air, by applying as a dressing some material capable of destroying the life of the floating particles."

Diseased Silkworms: Another Triumph

While it was a purely intellectual process that had led Pasteur to the conviction that microbes can cause disease in man, it was through accidental circumstances that he came to work on an actual disease. But his first patients were not human beings, they were silkworms! The production of silk from silkworms was then an important agricultural industry in certain regions of the center and south of France. However, toward the middle of the nineteenth century a mysterious disease began to attack the French silkworm nurseries. By 1865 the disease had spread to most silkworm-producing areas, and the industry was near ruin in France, and also, to a lesser degree, in the rest of Western Europe.

One of Pasteur's former professors of chemistry, Jean Baptiste Dumas, came from the afflicted region, and asked him as a favor to head a commission organized by the Ministry of Agriculture to investigate the problem. Needless to say, Pasteur knew nothing of silkworms or of their diseases, but he accepted the challenge. In part, his acceptance came from a desire to meet the wishes of his respected master, and to justify the faith that he had put in him. To Pasteur's remark that he was totally unfamiliar with the subject, Dumas had replied one day: "So much the better! For ideas, you will have only those which shall come to you as a result of your own observations!"

It is probable also that Pasteur welcomed the opportunity to approach the field of experimental pathology, as is suggested by a sentence in his letter of acceptance: "The subject . . . may even come within the range of my present studies." He had long foreseen that his work on fermentation would be of significance in the study of the physiological and pathological processes of man and animals. But he was aware of his unfamiliarity with biological problems, and Dumas' insistence helped him to face an experience that he both desired and dreaded.

The studies of silkworm diseases lasted from 1865 to 1870. The detailed account that I have presented in my earlier biography of Pasteur illustrates how they constituted one of the most dramatic and spectacular feats of his scientific life. Here I shall have to limit myself to a few dogmatic and brief statements which in their bareness cannot convey the intellectual and emotional intensity of these years.

Most of the work on silkworms was carried out in a rather primitive house converted into a makeshift laboratory, right in the heart of the silkworm district, in the remote and mountainous Cévennes region. There Pasteur had to familiarize himself with the anatomy and physiology of the worms, and with the techniques of silk production.

After three years of heartbreaking work, he established that there were at least two entirely different diseases, one the *pébrine* caused by a parasite protozoan, another the *flacherie,* primarily nutritional in origin. He worked out very effective and simple techniques for breeding worms not contaminated by the protozoan of *pébrine,* and for improving hygienic conditions in the silkworm nurseries. He organized a vigorous educational campaign to teach the silkworm producers how to apply his procedures under practical conditions, and simultaneously he engaged in passionate controversies with those who denied the value of his work. Because of the urgency of the practical problems, he was under the public eye all the time, compelled to divulge the laboratory discoveries as soon as they were made and to express opinions as to how they were applicable to industrial and agricultural practices.

Personal Tragedy: The Indomitable Will

During the same period multiple tragedies came to afflict his personal life. In 1865 he had lost his father and one of his daughters, Camille, then two years old. Another daughter, Cecile, died of typhoid fever at the age of twelve in May 1866. As the weight of these sorrows and the burden of the immense responsibilities which he had undertaken were leaving a mark on his health, Madame Pasteur, accompanied by their last surviving daughter, Marie-Louise, came to join the hard-working group around her husband. Then in 1868 Pasteur was stricken by a cerebral hemorrhage, which endangered his life and caused a permanent paralysis of the left arm and leg. As soon as he began to regain his faculties, a week after the attack of paralysis, he dictated a scientific communication to his student Gernez, who was watching over him during the night. Within a few weeks, he started again for the Cévennes mountains to resume his studies of silkworm diseases, despite the difficulties of the trip, the lack of comfort in his provincial quarters, and contrary to the advice of his physicians. This performance revealed once more that Pasteur was a man of indomitable will. It was not only his opponents that he wanted to overpower; it was also nature—it was himself.

There is no doubt that Pasteur's studies of silkworm diseases had great practical results and thus constitute the first practical triumph of laboratory science in the control of disease. But as in the case of the potato blight, these studies did not affect medical thinking. For most physicians there was no relation between the ills of mankind and the death of silkworms, but this was not Pasteur's opinion. He was aware that the work on silkworm diseases had been his apprenticeship in the study of pathological problems, and he was wont to tell those who later came to work in his laboratory: "Read the studies on silkworm diseases; it will be, I believe, a good preparation for the investigations that we are about to undertake."

Chapter 11

The Germ Theory
Is Established

We are now in a better situation to evaluate
the events of 1877. Contrary to general belief, the
year does not deserve a place in history for the first
demonstration that microbes can cause disease.
This had been shown for the potato blight in 1850
and for the *pébrine* of silkworms in 1868. What
does make the years 1876–77 a landmark in the
history of medicine is the fact that for the first time
a microbe was shown to be capable of causing an
important disease affecting higher animals and
men. The disease was anthrax, then very common
on farms all over Europe. Strangely enough, it
turned out that just as Pasteur was beginning to
work on anthrax, its microbial origin was also
being studied by a young German physician who
was soon to become immensely famous, Robert
Koch. Let us salute in passing this great German
scientist who shares with Pasteur the honor of having founded medical microbiology. To symbolize
the magnitude of Koch's discoveries, we need only

mention that shortly after the completion of his studies on anthrax he electrified the world by discovering the microbes responsible for cholera and for tuberculosis—two of the most destructive enemies of mankind.

Anthrax: A Final Proof

In reality, several veterinarians and physicians had suspected long before Pasteur and Koch that bacteria were responsible for anthrax. They had seen bacteria in the blood and organs of sick animals, and, furthermore, they had transferred the disease by injecting into healthy animals a few drops of infected blood. But, for a number of technical reasons beyond the scope of this book, these observations were far from convincing, and it took the experimental genius of Koch and Pasteur to demonstrate once and for all what the observation of their predecessors had merely suggested.

Koch's great experiment was to sow fragments of tissues from sick animals into a drop of serum of normal rabbits. He saw that bacteria similar to those originally present in the organs multiplied extensively in the serum and with the culture thus obtained he inoculated another drop of serum. After repeating the process eight times he found to his great satisfaction that the last culture injected into a healthy mouse was as capable of producing anthrax as was blood taken directly from an animal just dead of the disease. These experiments appeared convincing, but despite their thoroughness and elegance, they still left a loophole for those who believed that there was in the blood something other than the bacteria capable of inducing anthrax. Although Koch had transferred his cultures eight times in succession, this was not sufficient to rule out the possibility that some hypothetical component of the blood had been carried over from the original drop and was responsible, instead of the bacteria, for transmitting the infection to the inoculated animal. It was this debatable point that Pasteur's experiments were designed to settle.

Pasteur knew from his earlier studies on spontaneous generation that the blood of a healthy animal, taken aseptically during life and added to any kind of nutrient fluid, would not putrefy or give rise to any living microorganism. He expected, therefore, that the blood of an anthrax animal handled with aseptic precautions should give cultures containing only the anthrax bacillus. Experiment soon showed this to be so, and showed also that rapid and abundant growth of the bacillus could be obtained by cultivating it in neutral urine; these cultures could be readily maintained through many generations by transfers in the same medium. Pasteur added one drop of blood to fifty cubic centimeters (nearly two ounces) of sterile urine and then, after incubation and multiplication of the bacilli, transferred one drop of this culture into a new flask containing fifty cubic centimeters of urine. After repeating this process one hundred times in succession, he arrived at a culture in which the dilution of the original blood was so great—of the order of 1 part in 100^{100}—that not even one molecule of it was left in the final material. Only the bacteria could escape the dilution, because they continued to multiply with each transfer. And yet, a drop of the hundredth culture killed a guinea pig or a rabbit as rapidly as a drop of the original infected blood, thus demonstrating that the "virulence principle" rested in the bacterium, or was produced by it.

Pasteur devised many other ingenious experiments to secure additional evidence that the anthrax bacillus was the cause of disease. He filtered cultures through membranes fine enough to hold back the bacteria and showed that the clear filtrate injected into a rabbit did not make it sick. He allowed flasks of culture to rest undisturbed in places at low and constant temperature, until the bacteria had settled to the bottom; again the clear supernatant fluid was found incapable of establishing the disease in experimental animals, but a drop of the deposit, containing the bacterial bodies, killed them with anthrax. These results constituted the strongest possible evidence that the anthrax bacillus itself was responsible for the infection. The germ theory of disease was now firmly established.

Rabies: The Discovery of Filterable Viruses

The three decades that followed the original studies on anthrax saw the discovery of many other bacterial agents of disease by Pasteur, Koch, their associates, and their followers. We shall not review here the spectacular achievements of this period, which has been called the "golden era of microbiology" and which has had such import for the welfare of mankind. Startling as they were, these discoveries constitute merely the technical exploitation of the fundamental methods established by Koch and Pasteur, methods which rapidly became standard practice in the bacteriological laboratories of the world. It is of extraordinary interest, however, that the next great theoretical advance in the germ theory of disease was to be made by Pasteur himself when he discovered that disease can be caused by agents so small as to be invisible under the microscope and able to pass through filters, and so peculiar as to fail to grow in the ordinary culture media of the bacteriologists. These agents of disease are now known as filterable viruses.

The new discovery came from the study of rabies. Rabies was then known as a disease contracted by man or a few species of animals from the bite of rabid dogs or wolves. Bacteriological studies—and this must have been very disheartening—failed to reveal to Pasteur a bacterial cause for rabies. Attempts were made to cultivate a microorganism in spinal fluid, and even in fresh nerve substance obtained from normal animals, but all in vain. His failure is not to be wondered at, for it is now known that rabies is caused by a filterable virus, which cannot be seen by ordinary microscopy, and which has not yet been cultivated in life-less bacteriological media. With an uncommon and truly admirable intellectual agility, Pasteur then gave up the *in vitro* cultural techniques, to the development of which he had contributed so much. Heretofore, he had emphasized the neces-sity of discovering for each type of microorganism the nutrient medium most selectively adapted to its cultivation. He now conceived the idea of using the susceptible tissues of experimental animals, in-stead of sterile nutrient solutions, to cultivate the virus of the disease; the concept of selectivity of cultural conditions was thus simply carried over from lifeless media to receptive living cells.

Extension of the Experimental Method

The general symptoms of rabies suggested that the nervous system was attacked during the dis-ease. Nerve tissue seemed to be an ideal medium for the virus of rabies, and to fulfill the condition of selectivity, which was the foundation of the cul-tural method. As the main problem was to gain access to this tissue under aseptic conditions, the surest way was to attempt to inoculate dogs under the dura mater (the fibrous membrane surround-ing the brain), by boring a hole through the skull. "The thought that the skull of a dog was to be perforated was disagreeable to him," wrote his as-sistant, Emile Roux. "He desired intensely that the experiment be made, but he dreaded to see it un-dertaken. I performed it one day in his absence;

the next day, when I told him that the intracranial inoculation presented no difficulty, he was moved with pity for the dog: 'Poor beast. Its brain is certainly badly wounded. It must be paralyzed.' Without replying, I went below to look for the animal and had him brought into the laboratory. Pasteur did not love dogs; but when he saw this one full of life, curiously ferreting about everywhere, he showed the greatest satisfaction and straightaway lavished upon him the kindest words."

The dog inoculated by trephination developed rabies fourteen days later, and all the dogs treated in the same fashion behaved in a similar manner. Now that the cultivation of the virus in the animal body was possible the work could progress at a rapid pace, as in the case of anthrax, and other bacterial diseases.

Thus was discovered a technique for the cultivation of an unknown infectious agent in the receptive tissues of a susceptible animal. This technique has permitted the study of those agents of disease that are not cultivable in lifeless media, and has brought them within the fold of the germ theory of disease. The demonstration that invisible viruses could be handled almost as readily as cultivable bacteria was a great technical feat, and its theoretical and practical consequences have been immense. Even more impressive, perhaps, is the spectacle of Pasteur, then almost sixty years of age and semiparalyzed, attacking with undiminished vigor and energy a technical problem for which his previous experience had not prepared him.

Throughout his life the concept of selectivity of chemical and biological reactions had served him as the master key to open the doors through which were revealed many of nature's secrets. From the separation of left- and right-handed crystals of tartaric acid by selective procedures or agents, through the cultivation of yeast and of various bacteria in chemically defined media, to the differentiation of the anthrax bacillus from other microorganisms by infection of experimental animals, he had in the course of twenty-five years applied the concept of selectivity to many different situations. The propagation of the rabies virus in receptive nervous tissue demonstrated that the same concept, if used with imagination, was applicable to still other biological problems. In his hands, the experimental method was not a set of recipes, but a living philosophy adaptable to the ever-changing circumstances of natural phenomena.

Chapter 12

The Birth of Immunology

One of the first bacterial diseases that Pasteur undertook to study after anthrax was fowl cholera. He had no difficulty isolating its causative agent, and there would be no reason to single out this disease for particular discussion, if it were not for the fact that its study led to the discovery of vaccination—an achievement as remarkable in its practical consequences as in its theoretical implications.

Pasteur had begun experiments on chicken cholera in the spring of 1879, but an unexpected difficulty interrupted the work after the summer vacation. The cultures of the chicken cholera bacillus that had been kept in the laboratory during the summer failed to produce disease when inoculated into chickens in the early fall. A new, virulent culture was obtained from a natural outbreak, and it was inoculated into new animals, as well as into the chickens which had resisted the old cultures. The new animals, just brought from the market, succumbed to the infection in the customary length of time, thus showing that the fresh culture was very active. But to everyone's astonishment, and the astonishment of Pasteur himself, almost all the other chickens survived the infection. According to the accounts left by one of his collaborators, Pasteur remained silent for a minute, then exclaimed as if he had seen a vision, "Don't you see that these animals have been *vaccinated!*"

The Origins of Vaccination

To the modern reader, there is nothing remarkable in the use of the word "vaccination," which has become part of everyday language. But this was nearly a century ago. Then the word vaccination was used only to refer to the special case of injection of cowpox material for inducing protection against smallpox. We must stop for a minute, therefore, to retrace the steps that led Pasteur to see a relation between the protective effect of cowpox against smallpox, and the survival of the chickens in his accidental experiment.

In eighteenth-century England some people believed that anyone who had had cowpox, a skin infection contracted by contact with an infected cow and somewhat similar to smallpox, was thereby rendered incapable of contracting the latter disease. It is reported that Edward Jenner (1749–1823) was led to study the matter by the statement of a Gloucestershire dairymaid who had come to him as a patient. When he suggested that she was suffering from smallpox, she immediately replied: "I cannot take the smallpox because I have had the cowpox." Jenner attempted to give scientific foundation to the popular belief by studying systematically the protective effect of cowpox injection in human beings, and he soon convinced himself, and the world, that this treatment did in fact give protection against exposure to virulent smallpox.

Thus was introduced into the Western world the practice of immunization against smallpox by the injection of material originating from skin lesions in the cow; the word "vaccination," under which the method came to be known, is derived from *vacca*, a cow.

Jenner soon had many followers in England, but it was perhaps in America that the method received the most vigorous support. Benjamin Waterhouse in Boston took up the cudgels for vaccination, and, having received vaccine virus from England, he vaccinated his own family in July 1800 and dared expose his children to infection in the smallpox hospital in order to demonstrate that they were immune. In 1801 he sent some of Jenner's vaccine to President Thomas Jefferson, who had his own family vaccinated, as well as some of their neighbors and a few Indians.

Pasteur was familiar with Jenner's work, of course, and with the practice of vaccination against smallpox. And soon after the beginning of his work on infectious diseases he became convinced that something similar to vaccination was the best approach to their control. It was this conviction that made him perceive immediately the meaning of the accidental experiment with chickens. By transferring to man pox material from the cow, Jenner had so modified the human constitution as to render it no longer receptive to smallpox. Pasteur recognized that this effect was the manifestation of a general law, and that his old cultures of chicken cholera, which had become "attenuated" during the summer, had brought about some transformation in the body of the inoculated chickens making them less receptive to the virulent form of the microorganism. Jenner's discovery was only a special case of a general immunization procedure. More generally, vaccination could be regarded as a technique for specifically increasing the resistance of the body to an inimical agent. To make more emphatic the analogy between his and Jenner's discoveries, Pasteur chose to describe the phenomenon that he had observed in chickens under the name "vaccination." Thus, as has happened to many words, the meaning of "vaccination" progressively evolved from the description of a concrete procedure into the expression of an abstract scientific concept.

From Vision to Practice

The discoveries of Jenner and Pasteur have implications which transcend immunological science. They reveal in what subtle manner and how profoundly the behavior of living things can be affected by influences that reach them from the external world. Man or fowl, once having received a minute amount of material from cowpox or from the culture of a bacterium, are indelibly marked by this apparently trivial experience; they thereby become somewhat different living beings. Pasteur realized immediately that his observations of chicken cholera brought the phenomenon of immunity within the range of study by microbiological techniques. As he could cultivate the causative bacillus of chicken cholera *in vitro*, and as attenuation of the bacillus had occurred spontaneously in some of his cultures, Pasteur became convinced that it should be possible to produce vaccines at will in the laboratory. Instead of depending upon the chance finding of naturally occurring immunizing agents, as cowpox was for smallpox, vaccination could then become a general technique, applicable to all infectious diseases. Within the incredibly short period of four years, Pasteur succeeded in demonstrating the practical possibilities of this visionary concept for chicken cholera, anthrax, swine erysipelas, and rabies. I shall select a few of the aspects of the work on vaccination against anthrax and rabies to illustrate not the specialized techniques employed, but rather the amazing intellectual courage that Pasteur displayed in the prosecution of his work.

As soon as he had obtained an attenuated culture of the anthrax bacillus and worked out the technique of vaccination against the disease in his Paris laboratory, Pasteur expressed the desire to put the technique to the test in farm animals under field conditions. Anthrax was then a disease of great economic importance, and the possibility of finding a protection against it constituted a lively subject of discussion in veterinary circles. The germ theory of disease was still in its infancy, and few were the physicians and veterinarians who had any concept of the scientific meaning of immunization.

In the spring of 1881 a veterinarian named Rossignol succeeded in enlisting the support of many farmers of the Brie district, near Paris, to finance a large-scale test of anthrax immunization. Pasteur was well aware of the fact that many veterinarians and physicians were highly skeptical of his claims, and he recognized that many saw in the proposed test an occasion to cover the germ theory with ridicule. Nothing, therefore, could set in bolder relief his confidence and gameness of spirit than his acceptance of the incredibly drastic terms of the protocol submitted to him. Rossignol publicized the test widely, and the experiment thus became an event of international importance. It took place in the presence of a great assembly of people of all kinds, including the Paris correspondent of the *Times* of London, Mr. De Blowitz, who for a few days focused the eyes of his readers throughout the world on the farm at Pouilly le Fort, where the test was being conducted.

In the experiment twenty-four sheep, one goat, and six cows were inoculated on May 5 with five drops of a living attenuated culture of anthrax bacillus. On May 17 all these animals had been re-vaccinated with a second dose of a less-attenuated culture. On May 31 all the immunized animals were infected with a highly virulent anthrax culture, and the same culture was injected as well into twenty-nine normal animals: twenty-four sheep, one goat, and four cows. When Pasteur arrived on the field on the second day of June with his assistants Chamberland, Roux, and Thuillier, he was greeted with loud acclamation. All the vaccinated sheep were well. Twenty-one of the control sheep and the single goat were dead of anthrax, two other control sheep died in front of the spectators, and the last unprotected sheep died at the end of the day. The six vaccinated cows were well and showed no symptoms, whereas the four control cows had extensive swellings at the site of inoculation and febrile reactions. The triumph was complete.

As soon as he became convinced of the prophylactic efficacy of anthrax vaccination, Pasteur undertook to make himself the promoter of the new method. In order to convince those who wished to touch and to see before believing, he arranged for vaccination experiments to be repeated in different places in France and abroad. To the secluded life in the laboratory where the studies of rabies had already begun, he now added a public life not less active, involving detailed analysis of the results of field experiments, replies to the demands for information, answers to the complaints, and defense in the face of criticism and sly attacks, as well as of open warfare.

Thanks to prodigious efforts, anthrax vaccination soon became an established practice. By 1894 3,400,000 sheep and 438,000 cattle had been vaccinated with respective mortalities of 1 and 0.3 per cent under natural conditions of field exposure. Just as the demonstration of the pathogenic role of the anthrax bacillus had been the touchstone of the germ theory of disease, it was the vaccination against anthrax that revealed to the medical and lay mind the practical possibilities of the new science of immunity.

The Dramatic Prophylaxis of Rabies

It is, however, the antirabies treatment which is usually cited as Pasteur's greatest triumph and claim to immortality, and which established microbiological sciences in the popular mind and in the practice of medicine. Rabies had long had a firm hold on public imagination and was the epitome of terror and mystery. It was therefore well suited to satisfy Pasteur's longing for romantic problems. It combined a supreme challenge to the experimenter and his method, and the chance to capture the interest of the medical and lay public by a spectacular achievement. In fact, Pasteur was right in the selection of this seemingly hopeless problem. The Pouilly le Fort experiment on anthrax had rendered the public conversant with the doctrine of immunization, but it was the prophylaxis of rabies that made of microbiological science an established religion and surrounded its creator with the halo of sainthood.

In the first phase of the rabies work Pasteur showed that the spinal cord of rabbits dead of the disease could be rendered almost non-virulent by keeping it for two weeks in sterile dried air. Specifically, the technique consisted in keeping the spinal cord in a container with caustic potash to prevent putrefaction, and allowing penetration of oxygen to attenuate the virus. The famous portrait painted by Edelfeldt shows Pasteur absorbed in the contemplation of one of these flasks. By inoculating dogs with emulsions of progressively less attenuated cord, it was possible to protect the animal against inoculation with the most virulent form of virus. Under normal conditions of exposure rabies develops slowly in man as well as in animals. For example, a man bitten by a mad dog ordinarily does not display symptoms of the disease until a month or more after the bite. This period of incubation therefore appeared long enough to suggest the possibility of establishing resistance by vaccinating even after the bite had been inflicted. Experiments made on dogs bitten by rabid animals, and then treated with the vaccine, gave promising results. Would the same method be applicable to human beings bitten by rabid animals and still in the incubation period of the disease?

The story of the mental anguish Pasteur experienced before daring to proceed from animal experiments to the treatment of human disease has often been told. The decision to apply rabies vaccination to man was forced upon him when a young boy, Joseph Meister, was brought from Alsace for treatment on July 6, 1885, suffering from rabid dog bites on the hands, legs, and thighs. After consulting with physicians who assured him that the boy was doomed, Pasteur reluctantly decided to administer the vaccine. On July 7, sixty hours after the accident, Joseph Meister was injected with rabbit spinal cord attenuated by fourteen days' drying. In twelve successive inoculations he received stronger and stronger virus until, on July 16, he received an inoculation of still fully virulent spinal cord which had been removed the day before from the body of a rabbit that had died following inoculation with the virus. Joseph Meister exhibited no symptom and returned to Alsace in good health. He later became gatekeeper of the Pasteur Institute. In 1940, fifty-five years after the accident that gave him a lasting place in medical history, he committed suicide rather than open Pasteur's burial crypt for the German invaders.

The second case treated by Pasteur was that of a shepherd, Jean Baptiste Jupille, aged fifteen. Seeing a dog about to attack some children, Jupille had seized his whip in an attempt to drive it away, but was severely bitten; he finally managed to wind his whip around the muzzle of the animal and to crush its skull with his wooden shoe. The dog was subsequently declared rabid, and Jupille was brought to Paris for treatment six days after being bitten. He survived, and his deed was commemorated in a statue which stands today in front of the Pasteur Institute in Paris.

These two dramatic successes encouraged numerous patients to go to Pasteur for treatment after being bitten by animals known or presumed to be rabid. By October 1886, fifteen months after Joseph Meister had first been treated, no fewer than 2,490 persons had received the vaccine. Thus, like Jenner, Pasteur saw his method become an established practice within a short time of its inception, but as had happened to smallpox vaccination, the rabies treatment was immediately attacked as valueless, and capable of causing the very disease it was designed to control.

I cannot discuss here the very complex technical problems posed by the antirabies treatment in man; to a large extent many of these problems remain unsolved today. Granted the real difficulties associated with Pasteur's vaccination techniques, it is on much broader issues that his achievements must be judged. Pasteur had demonstrated the possibility of investigating by rigorous techniques the infectious diseases caused by invisible, noncultivable viruses; he had shown that their pathogenic potentialities could be modified by various laboratory artifices; he had established beyond doubt that a solid immunity could be brought about without endangering the life or health of the vaccinated animals. Thanks to the rabies epic, a new science developed which eventually led to the development of vaccination techniques against yellow fever and several other virus diseases. Even more important, immunization became recognized as a general law of nature. All these achievements were the fruit of Pasteur's boldness as an experimenter, and of his mental courage in the face of natural odds and of human opposition.

The Dream of "Chemical Vaccines"

After so many struggles, intellectual effort, and dramatic successes, almost any other human being would have judged that the time had come to stop, or at least to settle down to a well-established and comfortable routine. But this was not Pasteur's bent. Although tired and sick, and sixty-five, he began to think about new avenues of approach to the problem of immunity. His vaccines against chicken cholera, anthrax, swine erysipelas, and rabies consisted of living microbes, attenuated in virulence true enough, but still capable of multiplying in the body. In fact, Pasteur believed, and he was right, that the immunity elicited by these vaccines depended precisely upon the fact that they did multiply to a limited extent in the vaccinated individual. However, some accidental findings made in the course of this work led him to think that it might be possible to cause immunity by injecting not the living microbes themselves, but instead lifeless material made up of some of their constituents or products. For example, the bacteria of chicken cholera release in the culture medium a soluble substance toxic for animals. Would it not be possible to immunize the fowl by injecting this toxic material into them? With anthrax and rabies also some experiments seemed to suggest that immunity could be produced without multiplication of the living attenuated microbes.

Because of ill health Pasteur had to abandon experimental work before he could put these original ideas to the test. But his statements that the future of immunity might reside in what he called "chemical vaccines," in contrast to the living vaccines with which he had worked so far, clearly indicated the direction he would have followed if he had been able to work for another decade. Nor were these the thoughts of a senile, irresponsible man. Even in his lifetime others showed that immunity against diphtheria and against tetanus could be produced by injecting not the diphtheria or tetanus bacilli themselves, but instead their lifeless, soluble toxic products. Then it was found sometime later that immunity against certain bacteria and viruses could be produced by injecting these bacteria and viruses previously killed by heat or by certain antiseptics. One of the polio vaccines (the Salk vaccine) belongs to this class, consisting as it does of a suspension of polio viruses killed by treatment with formalin. Then finally, it has been demonstrated that immunity against some of the microbes that cause pneumonia can be produced by injecting a synthetic chemical substance similar in composition to the gum which forms a protective envelope around these microbes. Truly, the "chemical vaccines" dreamed of by Pasteur have now come into being.

From Folklore to Knowledge

Let us emphasize once more that all Pasteur's work on vaccination was carried out within a very few years, at the end of his scientific life, and against immense odds. And it would be appropriate therefore to take this occasion to review the qualities of mind and character that made possible this astounding achievement. But let us, instead, conclude this chapter, as Pasteur would have liked, by pointing out that the story of vaccination provides one of the most spectacular examples of the power of experimental science, and of the manner in which folklore evolves into rational knowledge.

For thousands of years it had been known that persons recovered from a given disease were more likely to be more resistant than their fellow men to the same disease. Either by accident or by trial and error, certain simple techniques of immunization had been developed to bring about this state of increased resistance. One of these techniques had grown from the knowledge among dairymaids in England that they did not develop smallpox if they had had an attack of cowpox—a folklore experience that Jenner had converted into a practical technique of vaccination. One century after Jenner, Pasteur guessed that vaccination against smallpox with cowpox was in reality the specialized application of a general law of nature—namely, that one can vaccinate against many types of microbial diseases by using related microorganisms of attenuated virulence. This generalization led to the development of general techniques for the production of vaccines. It gave birth to the science of immunology and encouraged chemists to study the nature of the substances in microorganisms that are capable of inducing resistance to infection. Thus, the biological science of immunology progressively evolved into its chemical counterpart, immunochemistry. In other words, 150 years of systematic experimental science transformed the empirical knowledge of the dairymaid into the refined understanding of the professional immunochemist.

This example makes clear that, while knowledge often begins with observations and operations within the reach of most perceptive and intelligent persons, it can grow rapidly, and in depth, only when pursued systematically by the techniques of experimental science.

Chapter 13

Further Applications of the Germ Theory of Disease

As we have seen, Pasteur showed very early in his scientific life an uncanny skill in converting the results of theoretical studies into practical applications. Just as the experiments on fermentation led him to develop practical procedures for preserving foodstuffs with controlled heating, so did the experiments on the germ theory of disease lead him to become involved in practical problems of medicine and surgery. The studies of vaccination which have just been recounted constitute the most spectacular phase of his achievements in this field, and also the most productive in practical results. But he devoted himself to many other types of practical applications, some of which have come to fruit only in recent years.

Biological Control and Warfare with Microbes

One of Pasteur's most original ideas was to use microorganisms for the control of animal and plant parasites. The first suggestion of his interest in this field appears as a casual laboratory note of 1882. It concerns phylloxera, a plant louse that was then destroying the vineyards of France and of the rest of Europe. "The insect . . . must have some contagious disease of its own," Pasteur wrote, "and it should not be impossible to isolate the causative microorganism of this disease. One would next . . . produce artificial foci of infection in countries affected by the phylloxera." Pasteur never followed this idea, but he came back to it five years later, with regard to the control of the rabbits which had become a plague threatening the economy of Australia and New Zealand. In a letter to an English journal, he suggested that the most promising approach to the eradication of rabbits was to introduce into Australia a microbial species that would start a fatal infection among them. "So far, one has employed chemical poisons to control this plague. . . . Is it not preferable to use, in order to destroy living beings, a poison endowed with life and capable of multiplying at a great speed? . . . I should like to see the agent of death carried into the burrows by communicating to rabbits a disease that might become epidemic."

He carried out a field test of his idea on an estate in France, having cultures of the bacillus *Pasteurella multocida*, which is virulent for rabbits, spread on alfalfa around burrows. Although many rabbits died after eating the contaminated alfalfa, practical reasons prevented him from going further with this technique. In fact, it is most unlikely that infection with *Pasteurella multocida* would have proved effective as a method of rabbit control on a large scale, because it is now known that this organism could not have established a widespread rabbit epidemic with a progressive course. Nevertheless, many attempts have since been made to control animal and plant plagues with other microbial parasites, and a few of these attempts have produced spectacular results—for a while at least. For example, the introduction into Australia and Europe a few years ago of the virus which causes the fatal disease known as myxomatosis has brought about a destructive epidemic among the rabbits in these countries. Although the ultimate outcome of the epidemic cannot yet be predicted, there is no doubt that Pasteur clearly visualized the practical potentialities of biological control of plant and animal pests through the activities of microorganisms. It is a sad commentary on the role of the scientists in the modern world that huge research programs are now devoted to the search for ways to utilize these potentialities in military conflicts. What Pasteur had suggested as a possible method of biological control of pests is now studied chiefly as a possible technique of bacteriological warfare.

Antibiotics and Aseptic Surgery

In the past two decades Pasteur's name has been mentioned frequently with reference to the discovery of antimicrobial drugs produced by microorganisms—the so-called antibiotics. All historians of the subject point to his original observation that cultures of the anthrax bacillus with which he was working lost their virulence when they became contaminated with soil microorganisms. Amazingly enough, it is never mentioned that his first realization that certain living things produce substances capable of exerting selective antimicrobial effects antedates his anthrax work by twenty years. In his very first paper on lactic-acid fermentation, published as we have seen in 1857, he reported that onion juice added to a sugar solution prevented the development of yeast. There is no doubt that he had clearly seen the practical potentialities of these observations, as shown by his statement in 1878 that "these facts perhaps justify the highest hopes for therapeutics." This prophecy was completely fulfilled half a century later with the discovery of penicillin, and today it is still inspiring countless workers all over the world in their attempts to obtain new anti-infectious drugs from microorganisms.

In view of the success of this prophetic vision, it seems at first sight odd that Pasteur never actually concerned himself with the development and use of drugs for the treatment of infectious diseases. The reason is to be found in his belief that prevention is better than cure. "When meditating over a disease," he wrote, "I never think of finding a remedy for it but, instead, search for means to prevent it." This was the medical philosophy that prompted him to devote so much effort to the problems of vaccination and of sanitation.

As he began to frequent hospital wards, Pasteur became more and more convinced that the very objects surrounding the patients were the source of dangerous microorganisms and that even the doctors and nurses often acted as carriers of infection. He—who did not have a medical degree— was bold enough to scold physicians on this score. In a famous lecture delivered before the Academy of Medicine in Paris he issued warnings which created a great sensation: "This water, this sponge, this lint with which you wash or cover a wound, may deposit germs which have the power of multiplying rapidly within the tissues. . . . If I had the honor of being a surgeon, impressed as I am with the dangers to which the patient is exposed from the microbes present over the surface of all objects, particularly in hospitals, not only would I use none but perfectly clean instruments, but I would clean my hands with the greatest care, and subject them to a rapid flaming. . . . I would use only lint, bandages, and sponges previously exposed to a temperature of 130° to 150° C." This memorable statement has become the basis of aseptic surgery, which aims at preventing access of microorganisms to the operative field rather than trying to kill them with antiseptics applied to the tissues.

It is not necessary to emphasize further the contributions made by the germ theory of disease to the development of sanitary measures. As everyone knows, awareness of the dangers of infection is now universal in our communities, and specialized control laboratories watch over the water we drink, the food we eat, the objects we touch, and the air we breathe, in an attempt to eliminate from our environment any microorganism potentially capable of causing disease. Sanitation has now become almost synonymous with Western civilization and there is no doubt that it has greatly contributed to the decrease in the prevalence of microbial disease during recent decades.

A Neglected Lesson

So great, indeed, have been the practical achievements that have grown out of bacteriological knowledge that there has been a tendency to regard the control of disease as absolutely dependent on the use of techniques directed against the microorganisms. In reality, however, there are many other factors to be considered in the study of microbial diseases. For example, the hereditary constitution of the patient, his nutritional state, his emotional equilibrium, the season of the year, and the climate are among the factors that can affect the course of infection. Today, many physicians and medical scientists lament the fact that, under the influence of the germ theory of disease, all these factors tend to be neglected and even ignored. I believe that if Pasteur were living today, he, too, would feel very much disturbed that his followers have emphasized only one aspect of his teaching, and have lost view of his broader philosophy of disease causation. Time and time again, he referred to the importance of the individual constitution and of the environment, and expressed a desire to investigate the role of these factors in the evolution of disease. Unfortunately, he was prevented from going into these fields by the enormous pressure of his experimental work with the microorganisms themselves—a task which monopolized all his energies even though it did not satisfy all the aspects of his genius.

Far from being hypnotized with the idea that microorganisms are the only factors of importance in medicine, Pasteur knew that men as well as animals, in health or in disease, must always be considered as a whole and in relation to their environment. This side of his scientific personality is so neglected and yet in my opinion of such great interest that I shall now discuss it in some detail, even at the risk of having to deal with rather technical matters.

There is no doubt, of course, that the methods developed to destroy, modify, or domesticate microorganisms have provided during the past century the most important applications of microbiological sciences to medicine, public health, and technology. However, it must not be concluded from these successes that no other approach is possible. Pasteur himself was convinced that there are other ways of dealing with the microbial world. In all his publications, beginning with the studies on lactic-acid fermentation published in 1857, he repeatedly stated the thesis—almost as an obsession—that the activities of microorganisms can be controlled, not only by acting on them directly, but also by modifying the environment in which they operate. It is to this aspect of Pasteur's thought, the effect that the "terrain" exerts on microbial activities, that we shall now turn.

The Importance of "Terrain"

In his 1857 paper Pasteur noted that when chalk was added to a sugar solution containing the proper kind of organic matter, alcoholic fermentation developed as early as the next day—spontaneously, as it were. In contrast, he observed that lactic acid was more likely to be produced from sugar when chalk was not added to the solution. With amazing perspicacity he guessed that yeasts as well as lactic-acid bacteria were commonly present in unsterilized sugar solutions in natural circumstances, and that while yeast was favored by a neutral reaction, bacteria preferred an acid medium. Extending this hypothesis, he recognized that other procedures could render the medium selective for one or the other type of fermentation; for example, by adding to it selective antiseptics. These simple straightforward observations, made at the very dawn of the germ theory, demonstrated that microbial activity can be controlled almost at will by manipulating the physico-chemical characteristics of the solutions in which microbes are present.

Pasteur's concern with the physico-chemical char-

acteristics of the environment continued throughout his studies of fermentation. Thus, he reported
that the very morphological appearance of yeasts
and of molds was much influenced by the cultural
conditions. Of greater importance, probably, were
his systematic studies of the profound alterations
that changes in availability of oxygen have on
metabolism—determining the yield in alcohol, in
organic acids, and in CO_2, as well as the amount
of cellular protoplasm synthesized.

While Pasteur's studies on the relation of environment to metabolic activity are fairly well
known, his intense awareness of the importance of
the "terrain" in infection is hardly ever mentioned.
Yet he repeatedly expressed his conviction that
the physiological state of the infected individual
often decides the course of the infectious process.
His intuitive understanding of this subject was extremely broad and took into account genetic and
evolutionary concepts of adaptation, as appears
from casual remarks that he made in many of his
public statements.

Physiology and Infection

Very early, Pasteur recognized that it is a biological necessity for living things to be endowed with
natural resistance to the agents of destruction
ubiquitous in their environment. As he saw it,
populations—be they of microbes or men—usually
achieve through evolutionary changes some sort of
adaptation to their environment which renders

them able to resist the causes of disease with which they frequently come into contact. Whatever the precise mechanisms involved, Pasteur took it for granted that the body in a state of normal physiological health exhibits a striking resistance to many types of microbial agents. For instance, he pointed out, the various body surfaces and the intestinal tract always harbor microorganisms which are innocuous in normal circumstances, but can cause damage when the body is weakened. Likewise, infection often fails to take hold following surgery even when antiseptic measures are neglected, because the body usually possesses a remarkable power to control foci of infection.

Pasteur had developed this belief in the relation between the general state of well-being and resistance to infection during his studies with silkworms. He had then noticed that in the case of the disease *flacherie*, the resistance of the worms to infection was decreased by poor food, excessive heat and humidity, inadequate aeration, and even by stormy weather. As Pasteur put it, the proliferation of microorganisms in the intestinal tract of the silkworms suffering from *flacherie* was an effect rather than a cause of the disease. He was thus anticipating George Bernard Shaw's remark in the preface to *The Doctor's Dilemma:* "The characteristic microbe of a disease might be a symptom instead of a cause."

Pasteur did not hesitate to extend these views to the most important of human diseases. He recognized that resistance to tuberculosis was an expression of native hereditary endowment, and was influenced by the state of nutrition as well as by other factors of the environment, including the climate. Even more boldly he suggested that the mental state of the patient might affect the course of many human diseases.

This point of view naturally led Pasteur to conclude that resistance to infection could probably be increased by improving the physiological state of the infected individual. He urged his collaborators to look for procedures that would increase general resistance. And he expressed the opinion that in man as well as in animals successful therapy often depended upon the ability of the physician or the veterinarian to restore physiological conditions favorable to natural resistance. "Should circumstances bring me again to deal with the diseases of silkworms," he stated late in his life, "I would undertake new studies to discover the physiological factors that affect their resistance to infection."

Although circumstances never permitted Pasteur to contribute much to this aspect of infectious diseases, he carried out at least one spectacular experiment having to do with the effect of temperature on susceptibility to infection. Puzzled by the fact that hens were refractory to anthrax, he had wondered whether this might not be explained by their body temperature, which is higher than that of animals susceptible to this disease. To test his hypothesis, he inoculated hens with anthrax bacilli and placed them in a cold bath to lower their body temperature. Animals so treated died the next day, showing numerous bacilli in their blood and organs. Another hen, similarly infected and maintained in the cold bath until the disease was in full progress, was then taken out of the water, dried, wrapped, and placed under conditions that allowed rapid return to normal body temperature. *Mirabile dictu*, this hen made a complete recovery. Thus, a mere fall of a few degrees in body temperature was sufficient to render birds almost as receptive to anthrax as were rabbits or guinea pigs. There is reason to believe that the interpretation of this change in susceptibility is much more complex than was assumed by Pasteur, but whatever the exact mechanism involved, his experiment illustrates how the environment profoundly affects the response of the body to infectious agents. In fact, I am convinced that this experiment will be regarded someday as the beginning of a new chapter in the germ theory of disease, a chapter concerned not with the properties of the infective microorganisms themselves, but rather with the characteristics of the patient that determine the manner in which the body responds to infection.

Chapter 14

A Dedicated Life

Pasteur possessed several personality traits rarely found together in one individual. His devotion to scientific research was complete, and, despite the stroke that partly paralyzed him at the age of forty-six, he worked with incredible intensity until his health completely failed. He was a masterful technician but also highly intuitive. He derived problems from industrial or medical questions, and never shied away from practical problems, but he also pursued the large theoretical concepts involved in his studies and thus reached fundamental scientific generalizations. He worked almost in isolation, with very few collaborators, but had an immense gift for public debate. In many famous controversies he overcame his opponents by the spoken and written word, and also by elegant and dramatic demonstrations. While worshiping experimental science, he also maintained that there exist spiritual values that transcend scientific approach—a thesis which he defended in a cele-

brated debate with the philosopher Ernest Renan
at the time of his reception into the French Academy of Letters.

Pasteur and Family

We cannot deal here with the more personal aspects of his life, even though this would make an
inspiring story. Let us merely mention that the re-
sponsiveness of his temperament and the warmth
of his feelings were manifested in a most engaging
manner in the wonderful relations that he had
with his father, mother, sisters, as well as with his
wife and children, his school friends, and his teachers. The following quotations from the letter that
he wrote his wife on the night of his father's death
may help to convey the warmth of his temperament.

"I have been thinking all day of the marks of
affection I have had from my father. For thirty
years I have been his constant care, I owe everything to him. When I was young he kept me from
bad company and instilled into me the habit of
working and the example of the most loyal and
best-filled life. He was far above his position both
in mind and in character. . . . You did not know
him, dearest Marie, at the time when he and my
mother were working so hard for the children they
loved, for me especially, whose books and school-
ing cost so much. . . . And the touching part of
his affection for me is that it never was mixed with
ambition. You remember that he would have been

pleased to see me the headmaster of Arbois College? He foresaw that advancement would mean hard work, perhaps detrimental to my health. And yet I am sure that some of the success in my scientific career must have filled him with joy and pride; his son! his name! the child he had guided and cherished!" Some twenty years later, the dedication of a memorial plaque placed on the house where he was born in Dôle gave Pasteur once more the occasion to express in public his feelings toward his parents. Answering the speeches of congratulation addressed to him, he replied in the following words:

"Your sympathy has joined on that memorial plate the two great things which have been the passion and the delight of my life: the love of Science and the cult of the home.

"Oh! my father, my mother, dear departed ones, who lived so humbly in this little house, it is to you that I owe everything. Your enthusiasm, my brave-hearted mother, you have instilled it into me. If I have always associated the greatness of science with the greatness of France, it is because I was impregnated with the feelings that you had inspired. And you, dearest father, whose life was as hard as your hard trade, you have shown to me what patience and protracted effort can accomplish. It is to you that I owe perseverance in daily work. Not only did you have the qualities which go to make a useful life, but also admiration for great men and great things. To look upwards, learn to the utmost, to seek to rise ever higher, such was your teaching. I can see you now, after a hard day's work, reading in the evening some story of the battles in the glorious epoch of which you were a witness. Whilst teaching me to read, your care was that I should learn the greatness of France."

Pasteur and Country

Pasteur's devotion was not limited to his family. He expressed repeatedly his indebtedness to some of his teachers; he remained attached to his native province, and above all he had a passionate love for France. "The thought of France supported my courage during the difficult hours which are an inevitable part of prolonged efforts. I associated her greatness with the greatness of science." Following the French disasters in the Franco-Prussian War of 1870–71, the Italian Government offered him a chair of chemistry at the University of Pisa, with a high salary and very great personal advantages, but after much hesitation he refused, "I should feel like a deserter if I sought, away from my country in distress, a material situation better than that which it can offer me."

His national pride was deeply wounded when France was defeated by Prussia in 1871, and he seized upon the occasion to point out to his countrymen that the disaster came in part from their neglect of science. Appealing to public opinion as well as to governmental bodies, he pleaded for more vigorous support of scientific research and of other intellectual pursuits. In 1871 he issued a

pamphlet in which he lamented the material circumstances that prevented young French scholars
from devoting their energies to academic research;
he contrasted the miserable state of laboratories in
France with the magnificent support they were receiving abroad and particularly in Germany; he recalled the prominent part played by French science in helping the country to overcome the
onslaught of Europe during the Revolution and
the Napoleonic Wars.

Some of the public statements that he made at
that time are meaningful for us today, when national survival depends so much on the proper attitude toward science and general culture. Time
and time again, he spoke of the "close correlation
that exists between theoretical science and the life
of nations." He pointed out that the material
prosperity that France enjoyed in the late nineteenth century had its origin in the discoveries of
the preceding generations, and that to neglect theoretical science was "to allow the sources of wealth
to go dry." Furthermore, while he emphasized science's essential role in the maintenance of national
wealth and power, he never lost sight of its larger
values. "In the present state of modern civilization," he wrote, "the cultivation of the highest
forms of science is perhaps even more necessary to
the moral state of a nation than to its material
prosperity."

He described with enthusiasm how, by virtue of
her leadership in scientific research during the fifty
years before the Revolution, the France of 1792

had multiplied her forces through the genius of invention and had found, wherever needed, men capable of organizing victory. And in words of overwhelming conviction he exclaimed, "Oh my country! You who so long held the scepter of thought, why did you neglect your noblest creations? They are the divine torch which illuminates the world, the live source of the highest sentiments, which keep us from sacrificing everything to material satisfactions."

A *Higher Dedication*

However, his devotion to the French cause did not blind him to the larger truth that science transcends natural borders and interest. He knew well that science is of equal relevance to all men, and is one of the few human activities of universal value. "I am imbued with two deep impressions; the first, that science knows no country; the second, which seems to contradict the first, although it is in reality a direct consequence of it, that science is the highest personification of the nation. Science knows no country, because knowledge belongs to humanity, and is the torch which illuminates the world. Science is the highest personification of the nation because that nation will remain the first which carries the furthest the works of thought and intelligence."

It was not in an abstract manner that he worshiped science. He said himself that it had been "the dominating passion" of his life, and that he had "lived only for it." On many occasions he found words filled with emotion to express the happiness that he had derived from his studious hours. At every phase of his life, he approached his work with such a sense of dedication that he could truly speak of "enthusiasm" as the internal god that had constantly sustained him. Across half a century, his voice brings a message which can help many of us today in the achievement of great tasks. "The Greeks have given us one of the most beautiful words of our language, the word 'enthusiasm'—a God within. The grandeur of the acts of men is measured by the inspiration from which they spring. Happy is he who bears a God within."

It was this enthusiasm, this belief in the greatness of the cause for which he was working, that made him speak with such love of the institutions of learning, the laboratories, and the libraries in which most of his waking hours had been spent. He was trying to convey this love to laymen when he wrote in an oft-quoted sentence, "Take interest, I beseech you, in those sacred institutions which we designate under the expressive name of laboratories. Demand that they be multiplied and adorned; they are the temples of wealth and of the future. There it is that humanity grows, becomes stronger and better. There it learns to read in the works of nature, symbols of progress and of universal harmony, whereas the works of mankind are too often those of fanaticism and destruction."

In his romantic student days Pasteur had thought that he would be devoting his scientific life to the solution of abstract problems pertaining to the nature of life. But circumstances had engaged him in other more concrete pursuits, such as industrial fermentations and the control of infectious diseases. In 1888, as he opened the new research institute to be named for him, he dedicated it with the following words: ". . . Two contrary laws seem to be wrestling with each other nowadays: the one, a law of blood and of death, ever imagining new means of destruction and forcing nations to be constantly ready for the battlefield—the other, a law of peace, work and health, ever evolving new means for delivering man from the scourges which beset him."

Four years later, his seventieth anniversary was the occasion of a solemn jubilee in the great amphitheater of the Sorbonne, attended by the President of the French Republic and by delegations of French and foreign institutions of learning. As emphasized by one of the official orators, it was not merely a great scientist who was the hero of the day, but a man who had devoted all his strength, his heart, and his genius to the service of mankind.

Unable to speak for emotion, and compelled to extend his thanks through the voice of his son, Pasteur then expressed for a last time in public his conviction that science would some day bring happiness to man.

". . . Delegates from foreign nations, who have come from so far to give France a proof of sympathy: you bring me the deepest joy that can be felt by a man whose invincible belief is that Science and Peace will triumph over Ignorance and War, that nations will unite, not to destroy, but to build, and that the future will belong to those who will have done most for suffering humanity."

Addressing the students, he recalled the rich satisfactions he had derived from his years of toil and expressed his undying confidence in the power of the experimental method to improve the lot of man on earth.

"Young men, have faith in those powerful and safe methods, of which we do not yet know all the secrets. And, whatever your career may be, do not let yourselves be discouraged by the sadness of certain hours which pass over nations. Live in the serene peace of laboratories and libraries. . . ."

Of His Time and Timeless

The account of Pasteur's deeds and words leaves the impression that his was truly an enchanted life —with prodigious achievements, both theoretical and practical, spectacular triumphs over his opponents, and a world-wide fame that made him a legendary character during his lifetime. We have seen, however, that all this had been gained at the cost of arduous and constant labor, against all kinds of odds and much opposition. Certainly also, Pasteur suffered in his later life from having been compelled by practical necessities to abandon some of the theoretical problems dearest to his heart. Time and time again, he stated that he had been "enchained" by an inescapable forward-moving logic that had led him from the study of crystals to the study of fermentation and spontaneous generation, and then of contagious diseases. Yet the desire of his early days to work on the nature of life had remained one of his haunting dreams. He came to believe that it was only through accidental circumstances that he was involved in practical problems—important of course, but not as deep in their significance as those he had visualized early in life. Pasteur's grandson, Professor L. Pasteur Vallery-Radot, has recently told a moving story which reveals the pathetic intensity of this inner conflict during Pasteur's later years.

"I see again that face, that appeared to be carved from a block of granite—that high and large forehead, those grayish-green eyes, with such a deep and kind look. He was partly paralyzed on his left side, and it was with this terrible incapacity that he carried on his research on infectious diseases.

"He seemed to me serious and sad. He was probably sad because of all the things he had dreamed of but not realized.

"I remember one evening, at the Pasteur Institute. He was writing quietly at his desk, his head bent on his right hand, in a familiar pose. I was at the corner of the table, not moving or speaking. I had been taught to respect his silences. He stood up and, feeling the need to express his thoughts to the nearest person, even a child, he told me: *'Ah! my boy, I wish I had a new life before me!*

With how much joy I should like to undertake again my studies on crystals!' To have given up his research on crystals was the eternal sorrow of his life."

In reality, however, Pasteur could not have escaped entirely the appeal of practical problems. He worked during the second part of the nineteenth century, a period when, for the first time, the findings of experimental science were being converted into practical applications on a large scale. As a man of the nineteenth century, he was bound to focus his efforts on those aspects of his science likely to yield concrete results. What is remarkable is that the urge to work on concrete problems did not prevent him from seeing beyond the immediate needs of his time, and from dealing intellectually with subjects that were not yet ripe for practical application.

All scientists, like artists, naturally reflect the characteristics of the civilization and of the times in which they arise. A few of the great ones, however, have visions that appear to be without roots in their cultural past and which are therefore difficult to explain rationally in terms of obvious direct influences. Yet even these creators should not be regarded as aberrations in the natural sequence of cultural events. They constitute rather peculiar mentalities through which emerge and become manifest social undercurrents that remain hidden to less perceptive minds. Some of them succeed in converting their visions—which are really signs from the social and cultural subconscious—into messages and products meaningful and of immediate value to their fellow men. They become then the popular scientific heroes of their own society. Others perceive the hopes and the tasks of the more distant future, but without providing precise or practical solutions. They give warnings of the problems to come, but these anticipations are usually not understood by their contemporaries and acquire meaning only much later. Pasteur belonged in all these categories. Because of his immense practical skill in converting theoretical knowledge into technological processes, he was one of the most productive men of the nineteenth century. By synthesizing almost unconsciously the known facts of biology and biochemistry into original concepts of fermentation and disease, he created a new science which immediately met urgent needs in his social environment. And by visualizing microbial life as an essential part of the ecological complex, he foresaw an aspect of science that is yet to develop.

All the discoveries that he made have stood the test of time, and some of his prophetic visions are now acquiring increased significance as we add new dimensions to the magnificent structure that he began to build. His writings carry a message that will encourage us as we try to reach beyond the conventional theories of fermentation and infection. His thought is still a living force reflected in many phases of contemporary biochemical, biological, and medical science. To him can be applied the words that he once used in writing of his great fellow countryman, the chemist Antoine Lavoisier: "His scientific creation remains eternally young. Certain details of it may have aged, as have the fashions of yesteryear, but its spirit and its method will survive. They constitute one of the great achievements of human thought."

INDEX

Académie Française. *See* French Academy of Letters.

Academy of Medicine, 132

Academy of Sciences, 25, 28–29

Acetic acid, 43, 66, 83, 86; of vinegar, 71

Acetone, 77

Acidity, 45

Acids: acetic, 43, 66, 83, 86; amino, 78; butyric, 84, 86; carbonic, 81; citric, 77; gluconic, 77–79; lactic, 43, 44, 48, 77, 88, 90; organic, 77; paratartaric, 25; phosphoric, 82; racemic, 25–29

Aeration, 79, 83, 84–87

Aerobic life, 85

Air, toxic, 84

Albumin, 75

Alcohol, 46, 47, 79, 86, 88; amyl, 42; in non-organic medium, 83; oxidation, 66

Alcoholic fermentation, 40, 41, 42, 43, 48, 51, 65, 81; and chalk, 135

Alkalinity, 45

Amino acids, production of, 78

Ammonia, 29, 75, 82, 83

Ampère, 16

Amyl alcohol, optical activity of, 42

Anaerobic life, 84–87

Animals: diseases, 53; pests, 129–30; tissue, 90

Annalen der Chemie, 81

Anthrax, 94, 105–8, 118; bacillus, 107, 117, 131; in hens, 138–39; immunization, 113–14, 118–20; and temperature, 138–39; vaccination, 118–20

Antibiotics, 48, 78, 131

Antiseptics, 46, 68, 132; and vaccines, 125

Antiseptic treatment system, 99, 100

Appert, M., 71

Applied science, 41, 69, 140

Aseptic surgery, 131–32

Aspergillus niger, 90

Asymmetric synthesis, 38

Asymmetry: molecules, 37, 39; of universe, 35–37

Atmosphere, septic property of, 100

Australia, 129, 130

Bacteria, 59; and anthrax, 106–8; lactic-acid, 66; virulence principle, 108

Bacteriological warfare, 130

Bacteriology, 63, 64

Beer, 41, 77, 79, 82; alterations in, 67

Beet juice, fermented, 42, 54

Bernard, Claude, 56

Berzelius, 43

Beverages, preservation of, 72

Bigo, M., 42, 47

Biochemistry, 16, 38, 39, 48, 81–93; and asymmetry, 37–39; landmark, 46; and life, 81–93

Biological specificity, 39, 92

Biology, 16, 42; landmark, 46; selectivity of reactions, 112

Biot, Jean Baptiste, 24, 25, 28–30

Blood, 63; infected, 106–8

Bonaparte, Napoleon, 18. *See also* Napoleon I.

Brine, 71

Butanol, 77

Butyric acid, 84, 86, 88

Butyric fermentation, 84–85

Calcium paratartrate, 34

Canning, 71, 72; industry, 71

Carbon dioxide, 75

Carbonic acid, 81

Catalyst, 43

Cells, 91

Cellular Pathology, 49

Cévennes mountains, 102, 104

Chamberland, 119

Chappius, M., 23, 36

Cheese making, 77

Chemical vaccines, 124–26

Chemistry, 21, 42, 112; self-reproducing reactions, 62

Cholera, 106, 113, 117

Citric acid, commercial production of, 77

Claviceps purpurea, 78

Climate, 137, 138

Cocoa beans, 77

Contagious diseases, 95, 99

Contamination, 61, 65

Cowpox, 114, 126

Crystallography, 23–30

Crystals: fractionation, 27, 34–35; optical activity, 24, 27, 29–30; physico-chemical properties, 21

Cultural medium, 82, 83

Cultures: of anthrax, 106–8; attenuated, 116, 117, 118; selectivity of conditions, 110

Darwin, Charles, 49

De Blowitz, 118

Decomposition, 61, 75, 100–1

Delafosse, 24

Desiccation, 71

Diastases, 78

Differential behavior, 39

Dilute alcohol, 83

Diseases, 53, 94–104; germ theory of, 48, 63; infections, 39, 48; resistance to, 136–37; sanitary practices, 95–96; transmission of, 95

Dogs, 110–11

Dôle, France, 15, 142

Drugs, 77–78; and microorganisms, 131; production of, 48

Dumas, Jean Baptiste, 101, 102

Ecole Normale Supérieure, 17, 21, 31, 50, 81, 90

Edelfeldt, Albert, 19, 121

Electricity, 16

Empiricism, 72, 126–27

Encyclopedia Americana, the year 1857, 48, 49

Energy, production of, 89, 90

England, 16, 115

Environment, and microorganisms, 134–39

Enzymes, 77, 78
Epidemiology, 63
Ergot, 78
Etudes sur la bière, ses maladies les causes qui les provoquent. Procédés pour la rendre inaltérable, avec une théorie nouvelle de la fermentation, 67
Europe, 98, 105, 129, 130; Western, 101
Evolutionary theory, 49
Experimental science, 72, 150; chance, 34, 113–14; field work, 118–19; method, 22

Faraday, Michael, 16–17
Fermentation, 21, 39, 46, 61, 77, 135; alcoholic, 40, 41, 42, 43, 48, 51, 65, 81; butyric, 84–85; commercial production, uses in, 77–80; and contagious diseases, 99; defective, 47; diseases of, 66; lactic-acid, 81; oxygen, role of, 86–87; theories of, 43–44; of wine, 25; by yeast, 87–88
Ferments, 43, 45, 89; in beers, 68
Fibrin, 75
Filterable viruses, 109
Flacherie, 103, 137
Flasks, 52; swan-neck, 58–59
Flax, retting of, 77
Foods: and germ theory, 65; preservation of, 71–73; spoilage of, 72, 73; sterilization, 72
Fowl cholera, 113
Fractionation, of racemic acid, 26–28
France, 15, 19, 40, 51, 68, 70, 129, 143; neglect of science, 143–45; silk industry, 101
Franco-Prussian War, 67, 86, 143
Franklin, Benjamin, 52
French Academy of Letters, 22, 141
French Orlean process, 83
Fundamental particles, 38
Fungus, 78, 97

Gelatin, 75
German process, 83, 84
Germany, 49, 67, 83, 86, 144. *See also* Prussia.
Germs, 63
Germ theory, 48, 60–61, 69; of diseases, 94, 118; proof of, 107–8; of fermentation, 94; hostility to, 82; of putrefactions, 100
Gernez, 104
Gluconic acid, 79; commercial production of, 77–78
Glucose, 45, 86
Glycerol, 77
Goniometer, 28
Grapes, 54; fermentation of, 57–58; juice, 56, 82; and yeast, 56–58
Gray, Asa, 49

Heat, 68; and food preservation, 71, 72; and vaccines, 125
Heat-resistant spores, 59
Heat sterilization, 68–69
Hereditary traits, transmissibility of, 92
Hospitals, sanitary measures, 132
Human diseases, 53
Hypothesis, 44

Immunochemistry, 127
Immunology: anthrax disease, 117–20; folklore, 113–14, 126–27; rabies,

Immunology (*cont'd*)
120–24; vaccination, 113–
15; vaccines, 115, 117,
121, 124–25
Inanimate matter, 55, 76;
and life, 61
Incubator, 51
Industries: biological, 48;
canning, 71; of Lille, 40;
and microbiology, 65, 76–
79
Infection, 48; and physiological factors, 136
Infectious diseases, 39, 48
Ireland, 96–97
Iron, 82
Isomeric substances, 39, 92

Jefferson, Thomas, 115
Jenner, Edward, 114–15,
116, 123, 126
Jupille, Jean Baptiste, 122–
23

Koch, Robert, 105–7, 109

Laboratories, 40, 42, 51, 146
Laboratory science, 104
Lactic acid, 43, 44, 48, 88,
90; bacteria, 66; com-
mercial production of, 77;
ferments, 45, 46; fermen-
tation of, 81, 83, 86, 131;
in sauerkraut, 71
Laurent, Marie, 31. *See also*
Pasteur, Marie Laurent.
Lavoisier, Antoine, 152
Liebig, Justus von, 43, 82
Life: and biochemistry, 81–
93; chain of, 76; micro-
scopic, 59; origin of, 23,
36, 38, 54–55, 59, 61, 62,
91–92; oxygen, absence
of, 85; product of, 39
Light, polarized, 24, 29, 35
Lille, 41, 42, 51, 65
Lister, Joseph, 99–101

Levorotation, 30
Lead salt, 27
Lysine, 78, 79

Magnesium, 82
Magnetism, 16
Malaria, 95
Mankind, welfare of, 13
Matter: inanimate, 55, 61,
76; into Life, 61; ligneous,
75; organic, 42, 54, 74–76
Meat, putrefaction of, 54
Medicine, 16, 48; germ theory of disease, 94–95;
landmark of, 94; and
microbiology, 105
*Mémoire sur la fermentation
appelée lactique*, 46, 47,
48, 99
Meister, Joseph, 122, 123
Metabolism, 91; environ-
ment, relation of, 135–36;
oxygen, availability of,
136; Pasteur effect, 13;
processes of, 43
Methionine, 78
Microbes. *See* Microorganisms.
Microbial industry, 77–80;
physiology, 91; products,
76–79
Microbiology, 46, 120;
golden era of, 109; in-
dustrial, 76–79
Microorganisms, 39, 43, 54,
56, 63, 65, 73, 76, 92,
109; acids, in production
of, 77–80; animal para-
sites, control of, 129;
of attenuated virulence,
127; in biochemical re-
actions, 77, 79; in bio-
logical products, 68;
chemical reactions, 81; in
commercial production,
77; and diseases, 95, 105,
133–34; distribution of,

Microorganisms (*cont'd*) 63; environment of, 135; and fermentation, 66, 77; and food spoilage, 72; functions, 75–78, 86–87; and heat, 72; as links, 75–76; locations, 76; nutrient medium, 90, 110; alteration of, 135–36; organic matter, role of, 48, 74; plant parasites, control of, 129; power of, 74–75; and spontaneous generation, 54–64; structure, 91; terrain, importance of, 135; uses of, 76–80; and vaccination, 127; and wound suppuration, 99

Microscope, 26, 34, 42, 65, 84

Milk: preservation of, 72; souring of, 44–45, 54

Mineral elements, 90

Mineral salts, 82, 83

Mirror image, 37–38

Mitscherlich, M., 25, 29

Molds, 136; and crystals, 34

Molecules: asymmetry of, 35–37; glucose, 86; structure, 37–39

"Mother of vinegar," 83, 84

Muscles, 90

Mycoderma aceti, 66, 67

Myxomatosis, 130

Napoleon I, 15, 24

Napoleonic Wars, 144

Nature: economy of, 39, 79; mastery over, 14

Nervous system, 110–11

Neutrality, and fermentation, 45–46

Nitrogen, 76

Non-conservation of parity, 38

Nutrition, 138

Oersted, Hans Christian, 15–16

On the Antiseptic Principle in the Practice of Surgery, 100

Onion juice, 46, 131

Optical activity, 38, 42

Organic acids, 77

Organic matter: changes in, 54; and microorganism, 76; optically active, 42

"Origin of Optical Activity, The," 38

Oxidation, 83, 86

Oxygen, 90; and fermentation, 79, 85, 86; utilization, 86–89

Parasite protozoan, 103

Paratartrates, 25–28

Paris, 16, 17, 25, 50, 51, 52, 54, 117, 118, 123, 132

Pasteur, Camille, 103

Pasteur, Cecile, 103

Pasteur effect, 13

Pasteurella multocida, 129–30

Pasteur Institute, 52, 122, 123, 147

Pasteurization, 13, 68–74

Pasteur, Louis: aim in life, 23; and biochemistry, 81–93; and biology, 21, 42; birth, 15, 16; character traits, 13, 18, 20–21, 50, 104, 110–11; and chemistry, 21, 40; collaborators, 140; controversialist, 53, 103, 140; description of, 149; at Ecole Normale Supérieure, 17–18, 20–21, 23–31, 50; education, 17–31, 94; experiments: anthrax, 107–8, 116–20, beverages, 65–69, 86, crystals, 24–30, 149, fermentation, 41–48, 51,

Pasteur, Louis (*cont'd*)
56–58, 77, 81, 97, 98,
heat sterilization, 68–69,
infectious diseases, 39, 48,
53, 94, 104, 149, micro-
bial activity, 74–78, 80,
83, 97, pest controls,
129–130, rabies, 109–12,
120–26, silkworms, 101–
4, "spontaneous genera-
tion," 52, 54–63, 92, 97–
98, 149, vaccinations,
113–27, vinegar produc-
tion, 83–84, yeast, 82–83,
87–90; family, 15, 17,
31–33, 103, 141–43, 149;
and finances, 40, 51, 70;
French Academy of
Letters, membership in,
22; greatness of, 151–52;
health, 32, 103, 125, 140,
149; hostility to, 81–82;
and immunology, 113–14,
116–17; as industrial de-
signer, 69; laboratory, 51–
52, 67, 102; laboratory
techniques, 107–8, 110,
140; life, study of, 37, 91–
92, 149; marriage, 31, 32,
33, 103; microbiology, 47;
originality of, 23–24; as
painter, 18–20; pasteurization, 13, 68–74; patents,
70; as patriot, 53, 67,
143–45; philosophy, 40–
41, 53, 131–32; physics,
21; posts, 31–33, 40, 50–
52, 143; science, dedica-
tion to, 145–50; as sci-
entist, 26–28, 30, 40, 45,
55–56, 112; seventieth
anniversary, 147; and surgery, 99–101; vaccines,
chemical, 124–26; White
Knight of Science, 14;
writings, 46, 52, 67, 69,
86, 97, 131; quoted on

science, 69, 143–45, 147–
48
Pasteur, Marie Laurent, 31–
33
Pasteur, Marie-Louise, 103
Pasteur Vallery-Radot, L.,
149
Pathology, 102
Pébrine, 103, 105
Pectases, 78
Penicillin, 78, 131
Philosophy, and science, 62
Phosphoric acid, 82
Physico-chemistry, 16
Physics, 21
Physiology, 91
Phylloxera, 129
Phytophthora infestaus, 97
Pilot brewery, 67
Plague, 96
Plant louse, 129
Plant pests, biological con-
trol over, 129–30
Polarimeter, 28, 29, 30, 42
Polarized light, 24, 25, 29,
35, 42
Polio vaccine, 125
Polio viruses, 125
Potassium, 82
Potato blight, 1850, 96–
97, 105
Pouilly le Fort, France, 118,
120
Primeval ooze, 62
Proline, 78
Proteases, 78
Protozoan, 103
Prussia, 143. *See also* Ger-
many.
Public health, 21
Pure science, 41, 69, 140
Putrefaction, 61, 71; and
contagious diseases, 99

Quarantine, 96
Quartz crystals, 24, 26

Rabbits, 121; control over, 129–30
Rabies, 109–11, 120; vaccine, 121
Racemic acid, 25, 29; fractionation of, 26–28
Racemus, 25
Radiation, 72
Raulin, M., 90
Refuse, 76
Renan, Ernest, 22, 141
Research institutions, 52
Respiration, 21
Respiratory mechanism, 90
Retting, of flax, 77
Riboflavin, 77–78
Rossignol, M., 118
Roux, Emile, 32–33, 110, 119

Sanitation, 95–96, 132–33
Science, 14, 22, 34, 48, 116; applied, 41, 69, 140, 144; events of 1857, 48–49; facilities, 52, 104; nature of, 145; neglect of, 143–45; and philosophy, 62; progress in, 14, 52; pure, 41, 69, 140; in school texts, 15
Silkworms, 41, 101–3, 137
Soil, 76, 98; bacteria, 131
Specificity, biological, 39, 92
"Spontaneous generation," 52, 54–64, 92, 107
Stereoisomerism, 34–35, 38, 91–92
Sterilization, 58, 61, 63, 68–69, 72
Surgery, 99–100

Tartaric acid, 24, 25, 26, 27, 28
Tartaric acids, isomeric forms of, 39, 92
Tissues, as nutrient medium, 110
Trephination, 110–11
Tuberculosis, 106, 137–38

United States, pasteurization in, 70
Universe: asymmetry of, 35–38; riddle of, 22

Vaccination, 13, 21, 41, 113, 114–15, 118–20, 126–27
Vaccines, 115, 117, 121, 124–27
Vinegar, 43, 67, 77, 83–84
Virulence principle, 108
Viruses, 33, 62, 110–11, 123, 129
Vitamins, 77, 78, 91

Wines, 41, 77, 79; partial sterilization, 68–69; souring of, 65, 66–67; into vinegar, 54, 66
Wound suppuration, 99

Yeast, 42, 43, 45–47, 65, 79, 81–82, 136; and aeration, 79, 87; chemical behavior of, 87–89; growth of, in non-organic culture, 82–83

SCIENCE STUDY SERIES

BENADE, ARTHUR H.   Horns, Strings, and Harmony, S 11

BITTER, FRANCIS   Magnets: The Education of a Physicist, S 2

BONDI, HERMANN   The Universe at Large, S 14

BOYS, SIR CHARLES VERNON   Soap Bubbles and the Forces Which Mould Them, S 3

COHEN, I. BERNARD   The Birth of a New Physics, S 10

DAVID, JR., EDWARD E.; VAN BERGEIJK, WILLEM A.; and PIERCE, JOHN R.   Waves and the Ear, S 9

DUBOS, RENÉ   Pasteur and Modern Science, S 15

FINK, DONALD G., and LUTYENS, DAVID M.   The Physics of Television, S 8

GRIFFIN, DONALD R.   Echoes of Bats and Men, S 4

HOLDEN, ALAN, and SINGER, PHYLIS   Crystals and Crystal Growing, S 7

HUGHES, DONALD J.   The Neutron Story, S 1

HURLEY, PATRICK M.   How Old Is the Earth? S 5

JAFFE, BERNARD   Michelson and the Speed of Light, S 13

KOESTLER, ARTHUR   The Watershed: A Biography of Johannes Kepler, S 16

LITTAUER, RAPHAEL, and WILSON, ROBERT R.   Accelerators: Machines of Nuclear Physics, S 17

LUTYENS, DAVID M., and FINK, DONALD G.   The Physics of Television, S 8

PIERCE, JOHN R.; DAVID, JR., EDWARD E.; and VAN BERGEIJK, WILLEM A.   Waves and the Ear, S 9

ROMER, ALFRED   The Restless Atom, S 12

SINGER, PHYLIS, and HOLDEN, ALAN   Crystals and Crystal Growing, S 7

VAN BERGEIJK, WILLEM A.; PIERCE, JOHN R.; and DAVID, JR., EDWARD E.   Waves and the Ear, S 9

WILSON, ROBERT R., and LITTAUER, RAPHAEL   Accelerators: Machines of Nuclear Physics, S 17